AT FIRST GLANCE

AT FIRST GLANCE

**AN COLLECTION OF
POETRY & PROSE**

LUW Press

"We look not at the things which are seen,
but at the things which are not seen:
for the things which are seen are temporal;
but the things which are not seen are eternal."

-2 Corinthians 4:18

CONTENTS

MAJESTIC MAGIC

FLASH FICTION

Keri Montgomery

MARVO THE MAJESTIC CONCEALED THE flash paper in his left hand, holding it with precision behind the fold of his red-lined cape. The audience didn't notice. They never did. Instead their wide-eyed curiosity was focused on his lovely new assistant Ruthy, as she smiled in her sequined corset and puff skirt. She collected a dollar bill from a gullible man in the audience. One dollar was more than Marvo expected from the crowd of farmers—small town, Midwest, in the depths of the Great Depression, and not accustomed to the striped tent and fanfare of a traveling carnival. But Marvo knew from experience it was the mundane ones who loved the sideshows the most. They craved the spectacular.

Ruthy handed the dollar bill to the magician via his right hand, just as planned.

"Thank you, my dear," Marvo said. With a snap of his wrist, he brought the bill high to his left glove, along with a strategically hidden striking match—completing the action faster than the lazy gaze of the audience could follow. In a fraction of a second, the small match ignited the flash paper into a popping flame and a puff of smoke, creating the illusion of a burning dollar bill.

The farmers awed and cheered.

Marvo reached out and produced the undestroyed bill from behind a child's ear. More cheers. More approval. He extended his arms in a grandiose gesture, soaking in the accolades of his audience's praise. The applause belonged to him, and he deserved their flattery. But they craved more.

An ache tore at his chest. They needed all he could give . . . again. "For my final marvel," he announced, "I will make this beautiful woman disappear."

Hushed whispers spread through the crowd, mumblings of shock, interest, but mostly disbelief.

Marvo motioned for Ruthy to approach the long, black coffin near the back of the portable stage. She pranced over and gestured in graceful sweeping motions to the intricate carvings in the wood. As Marvo circled the coffin, he visually checked that the bracing table legs and escape hatch were concealed behind the lower fabric curtain.

Everything was ready.

"As you can see, the box is empty," he said. "Only a true magician can make someone disappear into another world and then return them to ours. This type of travel is more than mere magic. It is a majestic miracle!"

The farmers gave a nervous clap, which died into silence. Several children stretched high on their benches.

Marvo helped Ruthy climb inside the box, forcing the knot churning in his stomach to settle as she laid flat and smoothed the ruffles in her puff skirt. From the back of the room, a carnival worker played a continuous drum roll. Marvo closed the lid.

"Dim the lights, please!" he said.

A carnie ran through the tent, extinguishing the hanging lanterns until only a single light remained attached to the center pole. The audience shifted in their seats, silhouetted in near-darkness.

Marvo stood at the edge of the stage, lowering his chin. "And now, by my majestic power, the angelic and bewitching Ruthy will cross over into another world."

The drum pounded as Marvo smacked his hands. "I command the universe to take her away." He stomped his boot. "It is done! Lights, please!"

The two carnies raced to relight the lanterns. Mumblings filtered through the crowd as they eyed the black box. Marvo threw back the lid.

The audience gasped, and then began to cheer at the empty coffin. Marvo reveled in the applause until the last clap faded. If only he could keep the praise going, keep their approval and their hearts pounding in anticipation, and keep them loving him forever.

"And now," he said. "I will return the fair Ruthy to our world." But his voice quivered on the rehearsed line. Under his breath, he said a quick, ordinary prayer—one of pleading.

Aloud he ordered the lights, commanded the universe, and pounded his boot.

The coffin shook.

Marvo reached back, hinging open the lid, and lifted his free arm. "She has returned!" he announced.

A series of whisperings filled the tent, the crowd rising to their feet. Marvo waited, but the sweet applause didn't come. Instead, a handful of peanuts hit him in the face.

"You're a fake!" a farmer shouted.

A child threw another handful. "Look, he dun lost his own Ruthy!"

Marvo flipped around. Except for a few scattered sequins, the box was empty. He felt along the back lining until his fingers caught on the metal latch where Ruthy should have escaped through the back panel. The latch hadn't been opened. Dread filled every surging nerve, aching breath, and tense muscle in his weakening body. He fought against the shock pulling him to his knees.

A woman in the front row took hold of her child. "Mistake, I'd say. Not magic!"

"No refunds!" a carnie said, holding up his hands.

Marvo glanced over his shoulder for only a moment, not willing to face their sneering disappointment as the farmers grumbled their way out of the tent. He waited, back to the exit, until the last adult and child were gone.

"What happened?" the carnie asked.

Marvo double-checked the latch again—no tampering—then he searched backstage and behind the curtain where Ruthy was trained to wait for her returning cue. Nothing.

"I don't know," he said, sinking onto the stage and covering his face. Marvo simply didn't know what happened

4

when they disappeared. He never did. It was random. And yet, his cravings for the applause won the gamble over his better judgment every time. No matter the cost. "I'm going to need a new assistant," he said. "The box took another one."

HORATIO

Spiritual Essay

Tim Keller

I SORT OF HATE TO admit this, particularly given my good Mormon boy upbringing, but I've always looked at spiritual testimonials in much the same way I've looked at campfire tales. I mean, sure—it can be exhilarating to wonder after the ghost of some long-dead debutante. Or imagine a psycho with the hook for a hand may be just outside, or pray the gentle scrape/knock on the roof of your car is just the harmless brush of a tree branch in the breeze, despite the missing boyfriend, and radio warning of escaped lunatics.

Anyway, in campfire tales, logic eventually prevails. I mean, how many hook-handed guys are there, anyway? The field of medical prosthetics has advanced well beyond the hook after all, and even among those who may still wear them, how many are crazy, murderous, and (of course) right outside your car?

I've always believed the same logic should be applied to testimonials of spirituality. Getting lost, and then inexplicably remembering the way, having car problems in the middle of nowhere and praying just before a convoy of Christian tow-truck drivers rides to the rescue, tales of heeded promptings, the answering of the still small voice—these occupy the opposing sides of the same coin. Many if not most could be easily explained away by coincidence, or the psychological make-up of the personality in question.

Nice people do nice things. Period. Thing is, we just don't want to be cynical. It's like Bigfoot, the Loch Ness Monster, or Ancient Aliens—even if we don't believe, we want to. Folks just tune their logical minds out.

My father, though not formally educated, understood well the psychology of this particular phenomenon. It was, I believe, among the cornerstones of his considerable popularity as a Mormon High Council speaker. He knew how to stretch that story, to milk it for every last drop of credibility, and then present it as evidence absolute. Dad could have called the Holy Spirit to physicality if he wished, then shaken his hand in front of you. In fact, I hear he once did.

He's been gone now nearly three years, but every so often I catch him reaching out from the grave, like the time I was at church a while back, which in and of itself is noteworthy because it's a place I usually avoid.

Not that I fear bursting into flame upon entrance. I mean it hasn't happened yet, right? It's just that I served my time, and having done so with distinction, extricated myself; an early release for good behavior. I opt to keep my ecumenical communing somewhat more private. Even so, familial and friendship responsibilities require occasional sojourns to the chapel—things like funerals, the occasional semi-heathen wedding, and baby blessings, the latter of which had purposed my attendance to a fast and testimony meeting on the Sunday in question.

I sat in the foyer and listened to the service being piped in over the speakers, as is my practice for these kinds of events. The sofas and easy chairs are more comfortable than the pews, and since I'm practically never the only heathen in attendance, the service is more pleasant too. Plus the practice creates just enough detachment to keep the congregation from going, "the prodigal son returns!" all over me.

The bishop kicked things off from the pulpit and it was during this talk that his allegory, that of being a teenager summoned to go home teaching by his senior companion, began to sound familiar.

My mind drifted back to the 1990s and a late-night phone call I got from Mom. She'd forgotten yet again that while Dick Norse blared away in the background at 10-ish in Idaho, it was after midnight in Ft. Lauderdale.

"I'm putting your father on," she said. "You need to write this story and mail it to us as quick as you can."

With Dad and me both secure in the knowledge that the only way for either of us to sleep was to follow Mom's instructions, he began to talk while I scribbled feverishly away. Funny how things come together sometimes, the bishop was relating (via an *Ensign* article) his part of a story I wrote as Dad had narrated it to me over the phone.

It was a week before Christmas and I was finishing my day's work. The half-moon in the sky was shining on the snow as I fed the animals and brought an armload of wood into the house. The thermometer read fifteen degrees. I sat down to read the paper as I do every evening. It was warm and cozy, and the Christmas tree lights seemed to make the room more comfortable than usual.

Then the thought came to me, "You haven't done your home teaching yet."

"It's very cold tonight," I protested, "and I haven't made arrangements with my young companion."

I settled back to read, but once again the thought came to me, "You had better go home teaching."

Realizing it was a prompting from the Spirit, I put aside the paper and called David Kunz, my home teaching partner, who agreed to go with me.

I had to smile at that part of Dad's story. Not to diminish David's spiritual epiphany, but it's worth noting here that while David no doubt agreed, perhaps even readily, the merest appearance of choice was little more than illusion. Dad was doing Jedi mind tricks long before Obi Wan was a glint in George Lucas' eye. Dad could hail a kid off his bike on a hot summer's afternoon to haul hay. Yes, it happened, and more than once. Dad was doubly hard to resist when the spirit was upon him.

At the Baxter home I noticed Brother Baxter's truck was gone. When she answered the door, Sister Baxter looked worried.

"Where's Lyman?" I asked.

"He went fishing this afternoon and hasn't come home. I'm really concerned," she said.

"Let's go see if we can find him," I suggested to David.

Another aspect of Dad's success (again, not to diminish the whole prompting thing), was that he rarely taught from the lesson plan, preferring instead to make his visits meaningful in some personal way.

We left immediately and drove to the Lamont Reservoir, a mile or so from town. On the south side of the reservoir we saw Brother Baxter's brown pickup truck parked three or four feet from the water's edge. As we pulled up behind it, we noticed the engine was running.

"Can you see Lyman?" I asked.

"I think he's under the truck!" David exclaimed. "I can see his feet!"

Yet another advantage of the foyer seats was that I felt no need to stifle a chuckle as David, in the middle of his reading, was forced to refer to himself in the third person.

We jumped out and ran to Brother Baxter, who indeed was lying under the truck.

11

"Lyman, what's the problem?"

I heard a faint moan.

When we pulled him out, we saw that his hands and head were scraped and bleeding. His clothes were wet and frozen, and he was almost unconscious. I opened the truck door and said, "Let's try to get him inside." The weight of his limp body and wet, frozen clothes made this task very difficult.

"You drive my truck, and I'll drive Lyman's," I told David. As we drove, I tried to get Lyman to talk. "Tell me what happened," I said.

He only mumbled, "...don't know ...sure cold!"

As we pulled into the Baxter driveway, Sister Baxter hurried out to the truck and said, "Lyman, should we take you to the hospital?"

"No, just help me into the house." As his feet touched the ground, his legs collapsed, so we carried him in and helped him out of his wet clothes and into bed.

The next morning I drove back to the reservoir and found the fishing pole—with a nice trout hooked firmly to the line! I stopped by the Baxter's to give Lyman his fishing pole, complete with fish.

"What happened last night?" I asked him.

He had stepped from his warm truck, he said, to check his fishing rod. As he stooped to pick it up, his leg slipped and buckled, pitching him into the water. The shock of the icy water immediately paralyzed him from the chest down. He grabbed at the sharp rocks along the water's edge, cutting his hands and face, and finally managed to drag himself up the embankment and over to his truck.

Once there, he was too weak to get in. He pulled himself under the truck, hoping for warmth from the running motor. And there we had found him, just in time to save his life. Our Christmas gift to the Baxter family that year was a simple willingness to put aside the warm comfort of a fire on a cold evening and follow the promptings of the Spirit to do our home teaching.

The rest of the meeting consisted of the usual litany ranging from kids repeating parental whisperings verbatim to the kind of acrobatic, credulity-stretching "testimonies" familiar to attendees of fast and testimony meetings everywhere.

I ruminated again on the tale.

I supposed Dad could have just wanted to see his friend Lyman. If so, however, why bring David into it?

Then there was the fact that Mrs. Baxter didn't know where Lyman had gone fishing. Dad simply drove to Lamont. It was a decent enough guess, as it's close to town, but so are three other fisheries. One of which, the Johnson, was a known favorite of Lyman's.

Bottom line: At a time when he was most needed, Dad showed up to render assistance. What's more, he knew where to go when the man's own wife didn't, and that Lyman would likely need assistance when he got there.

The various coincidences and tendencies of the personalities involved go on and on, diminishing the likelihood of random chance as they unfold. Occasionally, instances of things like one-handed hook murderers and Christian tow-gangs defy explanation.

Three years departed, and represented from the pulpit via reading, Dad owned the room again.

And so for my final chuckle of the service, my mind wandered all the way to Hamlet. There really are "More things in Heaven and Earth, Horatio, than are dreamt of in your philosophy."

OCTOBER NOCTURNE

Light Verse

Shirley Manning

Don't forget to wake me at five.
You know how I hate the alarm.
I don't want to miss
whatever is out there –
witches in the woods
starlings with inky-brown feathers
plotting their day,
horned owls finally closing
their golden eyes,
bats hanging out under the eves
leaving droppings and insect wings,
fledgling robin down
scattered on the lawn by feral cats,
black widows creeping back in the corners
and into Elizabeth's shoe,
roaches under the Cocoa Pebbles box,
and a hunch-backed, bare-toothed raccoon
hissing at a skunk
that high-tails it
into the hollow.

AT FIRST GLANCE

SHORT FICTION

Casey Gasper

I SIT ON THE BUS and watch the raindrops race down the window. Outside, the traffic ebbs and flows like a dance. The day is almost done, and I will soon be able to divest myself of the self-inflicted torture devices, or in layman's terms, remove my bra and heels. I shift in my seat and breathe in the unavoidable smell of public transportation. It is a musty perfume of stale cigarettes, B.O., and just a hint of pee.

The bus brakes at the next stop and I instinctively scramble to grab my purse from falling off my lap. It doesn't fall, but spills a couple items onto the floor. I snatch my phone off the floor when I hear a voice that sends a pleasurable tingle down my spine.

"I believe this fell out of your purse."

I look up and see a man that I can only describe as an Adonis. A Greek statue come to life. He is holding my lipstick and smiling. I reach out to take it, but when our hands touch I feel a jolt and I am no longer on the bus clutching a purse, but sitting in a restaurant across the table from this beautiful stranger.

He's laughing. Hopefully I've just said something witty. The waiter refills our wine glasses and the Adonis reaches over and lightly touches my hand, and just like that I'm back on the bus, our hands still holding the tube of lipstick.

"Thanks," I say, breathlessly. I'm flushed, and I can't make out his response over the sound of the blood rushing to my head. He sits in the seat across the aisle and smiles once more at me before focusing his attention on his phone.

I have no clue what just happened. Maybe I'm having a stroke. A wonderful, beautiful, fairy-tale stroke. I put my lipstick away and try to focus on my phone, but matching gems just isn't holding my attention. I sneak another look in his direction. I think he knows because he is smiling again in a mischievous way. His lips look soft and inviting and in the midst of wondering what it would be like to kiss them, I suddenly am.

His arms are around me, and my body melts into his. This is clearly not a first date kiss. We stop for air and he brings his hand up to my face and strokes my cheek with his thumb; his eyes never leaving mine. We're standing in front of the door to my apartment. He opens the door, kisses my hand, and tells me good night.

And here I am, back on the bus. I shift in my seat again, and look out the window while I wait for the heat in my face to subside. What in the world is happening to me? I bounce my knee with a restless energy, and at the same time embarrassment flushes my cheeks for what I've made this stranger do in my mind. Surely, he wouldn't appreciate the boldness of my imagination. Although I'm quite certain that's not what's happening. This feels like far more than an overactive imagination.

I watch his hands in the reflection on the window. He has long slender fingers; I wonder if he plays the piano. A total generalization, I'm sure. Perhaps he uses his hands to heal or to create. But that train of thought ends when his hands are holding mine as we stand at the altar together. He says his vows and slips a beautiful diamond band onto my finger. I repeat mine and with a shaky hand slide his ring onto his finger. The pastor introduces us as husband and wife. The Adonis grabs me around the waist and bends me backwards for a deep and dramatic kiss.

The bus goes over a bump and I find myself back in my seat making eye contact with him in the reflection. I smile sheepishly and look away from the window and down at my hands. I splay out the fingers on my left hand as if I'm admiring the wedding band that was there seconds ago. Only there's nothing there now. I close my eyes, take a deep breath and run my hand through my hair. I really can't afford to lose my mind now. There's too much going on at work. Perhaps I can wait one more month before I take leave of my senses. That would really be the more responsible thing to do.

Like a kid to candy, my eyes are drawn to him again. Only this time he is looking at me. I avert my eyes to the advertisement above him and try to play it off as if that were the plan all along, and his face just happened to be in that path. But I can't help myself and I look at him again. He is still looking at me. His eyes are deep and inviting pools of blue. The bus slows down again and more people get off than on; walking between us; breaking our eye contact. But as soon as they pass, we lock onto each other again. As the bus takes off again he quickly gets up from his seat and sits next to me.

"Hi. My name is Paul." He holds his hand out to shake mine.

"Hi." I take his hand and feel a delightful anticipation spread through me. "I'm Miranda."

"It's nice to meet you, Miranda."

DISINGENUOUS BENEFACTOR

PROSE POEM

Robyn Butterfield

A SMALL GATHERING—JUST FORTY-FIVE, FORTY-FOUR alive. A wife, five children, twenty-three grandchildren, cousins, and spouses like me. No tears. Life running in snapshots: vacations, edifications, graduations. A prayer and scavenged ode from his abode. No tears. No clue of cause. No whispered indiscretions just leaving, lawsuits, living alone. Descent from embraced, to endured, to estranged—unexplained. No tears—except mine, I who barely knew him.

GHOST HERDER

Flash Fiction

E. B. Wheeler

THE 7TH CAVALRY MEMORIAL ON Last Stand Hill gleams bone white against the star-strewn darkness. Moonlight reflects off the headstones in Little Bighorn National Cemetery below. I study the etched names of long-dead soldiers on the memorial and shiver. Ghost herders. That's what the local Crow Indians call those of us who work here at night, when the flag is lowered and the spirits are free to roam.

The other park rangers have told me the stories. A headless soldier. A pair of pallid children wandering between tombstones. Hollow hoofbeats charging up Last Stand Hill, echoing down the slope where soldiers and warriors bled out their lives beneath the scorching June sun. Some people think the ghosts are re-enacting the fight or trying to protect the site and their legacy. Others say they just want to coexist, reach out to the people who are drawn here by their stories.

The other rangers promise that Little Bighorn will make a believer—a ghost herder—out of me too. They swear the ghosts try to communicate with them, especially when there's danger. I don't know. I believe in what I can see, and I haven't noticed anything strange in the few months I've been working here, just the occasional brass button or bullet casing glinting in the dirt. We leave everything in place. The battlefield is one vast mausoleum, soldiers buried where they fell or in the mass grave by the monument, left to find what peace they can.

An upstairs light shines from the old library by the front gates. The librarian usually shuts those off. I stroll down the dark hill and through the national cemetery where veterans of later wars rest. Cold rises around me. I rub my arms. The chill lingers over my skin, clinging to me, slowing my steps. It retreats when I reach the front porch of the library.

The windows are fastened shut, but the door is ajar. I touch the door jam, splintered where someone forced it open. My palms turn clammy, and I back up, reaching for my walkie-talkie.

"Hello?" I whisper into the walkie-talkie.

White noise. I adjust the channels, try a few more times, but I'm only greeted by static.

A shadowy figure moves in the dimness downstairs. I reach for my flashlight, wishing I had a gun. There's plenty of things in there that might be worth stealing to a Custer nut, and it's my job to protect the artifacts here. Goose bumps prickle my neck. I slip into the darkness.

The floorboards creak. Silence. A chill drifts by, bringing the smell of dusty paper. Behind it, faintly, I imagine scents from the library's past use: a morgue for bodies brought from abandoned forts for reburial.

Tap. Tap. Tap.

The noise comes from upstairs, like footsteps marching a slow drill. I hold my flashlight like a club and tiptoe toward the faint light trickling down the staircase.

Tap. Tap. Tap.

I creep up, my hands trembling.

A figure in black stands on the landing above, illuminated by the light coming from an upstairs room facing away from the stairs. The flashlight slips from my hand, clanks on the wooden floor.

The figure doesn't turn at the sound. He's staring into the room, his profile ashy, his own flashlight clutched in stiff fingers.

I edge closer. The black-clad figure shrieks. Drops his flashlight and crowbar. He crashes into me, unseeing, in his hurry for the door. We both tumble down the stairs, and I twist my ankle. The thief's on his feet before I catch my breath. I stumble after him, but he's gone.

My legs are shaking, and my ankle twinges. I have to report the break in, but I need to lock the building first. That light is still on upstairs, in the room the thief was staring at. The one that terrified him. My mouth is as dry as the old books on the shelves. I should turn the light off. I limp back up the stairs. My feet catch on the edge of the steps, but all I can see is the afterimage of the man's face, the terror in his eyes. I retrieve my flashlight and reach the landing, pausing before I approach the door, open just enough to let me see the far window. Light filters into the hallway. The cold metal of the flashlight presses into my palm.

The thief probably just freaked himself out. Maybe on drugs. There couldn't be anything in that room.

I stand in the dimness, the pain in my ankle throbbing in time to my racing heart, my ragged breaths the only sound. I just have to peek into the room. Prove it's empty. There's nothing to all those stories. One look, and I'll know for sure.

I don't move.

A hundred heartbeats later, the building is still silent. Waiting. I step closer, turn my head, and reach in blindly to flip off the light.

Silence, thick and watchful, closes in with the darkness. I follow the bright little circle of my flashlight down the stairs. The floorboards groan as I hurry across them. I slam the door, lock it, and limp for help.

The cool nighttime air fills my lungs, whisking away the smell of old books and old stories. I exhale and laugh at myself a little, wipe my hands on my slacks. I'll have to tell everyone in the morning what a fool I made of myself, though I'll never hear the end of the teasing. Ghost herder. Hah.

A breeze whispers through the cemetery, rattling the cable on the flagpole. The flagpole that will call the ghosts to their rest in the morning. I glance back at the library.

The light is on again in the upstairs window.

THE COTTAGE

FLASH FICTION

Josie Hulme

"You what?" My voice is very quiet. My wife knows this is a bad sign.

"I didn't think you'd notice," she whines. "You're never here. You never see them, anyway."

"They are my children! Of course I'm going to notice when they're missing!"

"It took you three days." She says it under her breath; she knows she's poking a bear.

I grind my teeth. "I've been in the forest cutting wood for three days." I didn't choose my second wife well. "Get out."

She sees my face getting red. "I didn't send them away with nothing," she snivels. "I gave them our last piece of bread to share."

"Get out!" I scream now, spit flying from my mouth. "Get out of my house! If I see you again, I swear to God I will chop you up and feed you to the wolves."

She scrambles around the couch, grabbing up a lamp, a clock. "Fine! I'm tired of living in this hovel! I'm tired of your stupid children. And I'm tired of being groped every night by your rough, clumsy hands! You're the worst lover I've ever had!"

She runs out the door, brown dress flapping around her legs, arms full of knickknacks. She'll drop everything before she gets out of the woods. I know how lazy she is.

I don't even watch her go. I run to the tree house I made three years ago. Empty. I check the children's regular haunts: the hollow tree, the swimming hole, the toadstool ring where they've spent many nights watching for fairies. All empty.

I spin in a circle. Thick forest all around. Where would they go?

I notice a line of ants, all carrying tiny specks of white. I follow the trail and find a bit of bread smashed in the dirt. A little farther, I find another piece nearly hidden by a fallen leaf.

"Oh, you wonderful children," I murmur. I race back to the cottage and grab my axe, and then I follow the trail of breadcrumbs into the forest.

The trees are close, and the underbrush thick. Game trails cross each other or join for a time before veering off through the bracken again. The bread crumbs are hard to find, and I have to backtrack several times. At each intersection, I kneel in the dirt to see the paths from the children's perspective. If I were a child, which one would I take?

The crumbs get smaller and farther apart. The sun has set, and the forest is dark. The woods are no place to be alone at night, even for a man. I don't allow myself to think about my children alone in the forest at night. A wolf howls in the night, an owl hoots its lonely song. I climb a large tree to wait out the dark.

From this vantage point, I see a light shimmering in the distance. I've walked these woods a thousand times. There should be no light.

I climb down and run, keeping my axe ready and my ears tuned to every rustle in the underbrush. It doesn't take me long to reach a clearing where there never was a clearing. The sickle moon shines, its weak light picking out the details of a strange little cottage.

Lemon drop daisies and lollipop trees fill the clearing. Gumdrops line a brick path. Peppermint sticks frame the doors and windows. Candy discs form shingles, and icing drips a lacy curtain from the eaves. The spicy smell of gingerbread fills the air.

"What kind of magic is this?" I whisper. As I pick my way through the sugar-dusted flowers, a scream rends the silence. I know that scream. Echoes of that scream still wake me in the night when my dreams take me back to the day a rabid wolf attacked my daughter. Gretel! I fear something worse has her now.

I rush to the cottage. My axe cleaves the door in two. A large table set for dinner dominates the room. On the far wall is a large brick oven. Waves of heat rise from the glowing bricks. An old woman is pushing my son into the oven. I can see smoke rising from his kicking shoes. My daughter beats against the old woman's plump backside. In two strides, I'm across the room. I snatch my son from her. She turns on me, saliva dripping from her snarling mouth. Curses fly at me, but her magic is only strong enough to trick children. It is no match for my rage.

She runs from me. My first blow severs her spinal cord. My second cleaves her head from her body. I turn from her corpse and gather my children into my arms, checking fingers and toes and kissing their dear faces again and again.

At last their tears are dry. "Wait outside, little ones," I say.

I stoke the oven until sweat pours from my skin. I chop up the old woman and put her into the flames. While she turns to ash, I destroy the cottage. We're due for a good rain. It will wash this place clean.

By the time I scatter the witch's ashes, the sun is shining.

Holding two little hands in mine, I listen to my children's chatter as we begin the journey home. Their story wrings my soul. I've been fooling myself for years. The woods aren't safe for innocent children. I can get a job in town—trade the witches and wolves of the forest for the criminals and crooks of the city.

The trail ends. Our little cottage, snug and sturdy, basks in the bright sunshine.

On the other hand, I could teach my children to protect themselves. They may be young, but they're strong and brave. That flat area there, to the left of the house—that would make an excellent sparring ground.

I breathe in the pungent smell of the forest. This is our home. We'll stay and fight.

SUNRISE, CHAIR, BANANA

LIGHT VERSE

Sue Stevenson Leth

It's just routine; Medicare requires a wellness exam
every year.
You have to be in the system in case you need a doctor
someday.

I'm homeschooled in Mammography, a graduate of
colonoscopy,
the Hysterectomy means no stirrups, just a prescription
for estrogen.

Dr. Tom Jones doesn't look old enough to have a drivers license,
wears hiking boots, Levis, plaid shirt. He's kind and
attentive.

"Do you fall?"
"Fall?"

"Do you have good balance, do you fall down?"
"Only when I'm skateboarding." His side glance comes
quickly.

"Remember these three words. I'll ask you to repeat
them.
Sunrise, chair, banana."
"OK, sunrise, chair, banana."

Ears, nose, throat, negative. Reflexes normal. Heart
abnormalities, none,
abdominal discomfort, no. I draw a clock showing the
time to be 1:15.

"Perfect, very nice. Any complaints, Mrs. Stevenson?"
"Yes, chronic UTI's, my bladder's a swamp, mosquitoes,
algae, the EPA. . ." His side glance discourages me from
finishing.

"What are the three words again?"
"Uhhhh, sunrise, chair, banana.
"How is your short term memory?"
"Perfect, not a problem."

In the shower this morning I remembered I'd already
been there.
Getting ready for bed the night before, I was wearing
two pair of underwear.

AT FIRST GLANCE

"Can you tell me those words again?"
"Yes, eggs, milk, bread."
"Hummm, the three words Mrs. Stevenson?"
"Oh, sorry, sunrise, chair, banana. I'm on my way to
Walmart."
Another side glance.

"Age activated disorders, negative. You're in perfect
shape for your age. Do you have an email address?"
"Yes sir."
"Good, you can go to *www.mywellness.com*
set up a password and find the results of your lab work."
"Oh, very convenient, thank you."

*Me, remember one more password? I left the water
running in the shrubs for three days.
I wrote checks on the bank where the money wasn't. He
thinks I'll remember lab work?*

At home, I'm wandering, muttering to myself, sunrise
chair, banana,
sunrise, chair, banana, wishing I could find the
bathroom.

THROWING IN THE TOWEL

Humor

Chris Todd Miller

I'M STANDING BARE-ASS NAKED IN the Gold's Gym locker room, and I've just uttered a blue-streak that would make a sailor blush.

This is not by choice.

Unlike most of the female patrons who parade about the locker room applying make-up and teasing their hair with their goods on full display, as if they were preparing for a PETA protest, I ended up in this state due to some atrocity I unknowingly committed in another life, and the Universe is now balancing the scales. I'm sure you've asked yourself the question, "not even a towel?" No, not even a towel. Had the new management not done away with the courtesy towels provided by the previous managers, I could be standing here with a modicum of modesty. Granted those towels didn't provide adequate coverage either but at the very least they would've afforded me my dignity.

Make no mistake; I did bring a towel with me. Regrettably, that towel is under lock-down, along with all other forms of woven textile that I may have used to conceal my lady parts.

How is it then that I find myself in my current state? Let us go back in time 90 minutes. Come with me, friends, to a kinder gentler world. One in which karma was blissfully unaware of me, and instead, giving a figurative bitch-slap to the creators of *2 Broke Girls*.

I always stow my gear in the lockers farthest from the showers. They offer a bit of seclusion from the other patrons and thus afford a hint of privacy. Today, before I could get to my locker, another woman spotted me and engaged me in idle chit-chat. I know this woman, kind of. We run into each other from time to time and share a platitude or two, but I don't actually know her name. I would have dodged her this time but didn't realize she'd spotted me, because I was looking at everyone's feet, so as not to take in the brazen display of flesh. I'm not opposed to a bit of girl-talk; however, today this woman approached wearing nothing but a towel—wrapped around her head turban-style (ironic, right?). "Hey, I haven't seen you here in a while," she said.

"Well, you know, life kind of gets in the way," I replied while inching toward the lockers.

"I know what you mean. Yesterday, I had a bunch of errands to run, but first I had a doctor's appointment. He kept me waiting 45 minutes then, I had to change into one of those paper gowns, you know the kind that open in the back? I hate those."

"There's never a good paper gown when you need one," I mutter. "Well, come to find out my wait was worth it. He found a mole under my breast that needs to be removed. I had no idea it was even there. Here, look."

She maneuvered herself so I could gaze upon the wonder.

I've managed to achieve a fairly healthy body image, and at times have even been proud of my girls, but the operative word here is *my* girls. I'd rather everyone else keep *their* girls to themselves.

I looked away. "Really, that's okay. I'm no dermatologist. In fact, I need to get changed up and hit the pool." I gave her a smile and managed to escape without checking for lumps.

I quickly changed into a one-piece Speedo and headed to the pool. I approached from the shallow end, but before dipping my toe in, I physically recoiled. On the steps was a discarded Band-Aid.

Another change by the illustrious new management—kids are allowed in the pool on weekends. Which is something I try not to think about, but every Saturday and Sunday those raging Petri dishes with their hair-trigger bladders are given full access. I gave the Band-Aid a wide berth, and got busy doing laps.

Upon exiting the pool, I wrapped my towel around myself and made for the sauna. Inside the cedar lined room I found several other women already enjoying the dry heat, and taking far too many liberties with the dress code. For fuck's sake this is not Finland, people! In order to return to the locker room, I had to pass by the pool. Reeling from the dry heat of the sauna, I failed to properly secure my towel and it plummeted from my baby-birthing-hips directly into a puddle of other patrons' just-exited-the-pool-foot-water. I was horrified.

The CDC ranks all diseases on a biohazard scale of 1-4, four being "an extreme risk." In my head, I was facing level 5. There's no way I would use that towel after my shower, so it was either go home in damp clothes, smelling like chlorine, and deal with inevitable split-ends the chlorine would cause, or sashay to and from the showers naked. I figured that this crowd would hardly notice and there was no reason to think of this as a walk of shame. Buck up buttercup.

You know how there are those moments when you cut corners because you're in a hurry? Like speeding through the yellow light to save a couple of minutes but risking an accident that could prevent you from arriving at your destination at all? Yet still you pray that your guardian angel will be merciful? Well, get ready to dial 9-1-1.

I picked up my towel between forefinger and thumb and kept it as far from my body as possible until I could stash it in a Zip-lock plastic bag (yes, I had one with me, large enough to hold a towel—don't ask). I then peeled off my bathing suit and headed for the showers.

You might be wondering if my anxiety was warranted. Turns out, at the very moment I went au naturel to the shower, a rift in the space-time continuum shifted the locker room to an alternate reality, leaving me alone with no one to bare-witness (ahem) to my brazen affront. The return trip was equally uneventful, yet I was eager to open my locker and end my public nudity. I planned on drying off with an extra t-shirt I'd brought. Feeling a bit smug, I spun the dial to those three blessed numbers.

It's not hard to tell where this is going. Regardless of how many times I spun the dial, my lock
refused
to
yield.

I know what you're thinking—it's a problem with the organic interface. Despite the panic doing a soft-shoe in my stomach, my mind was sharp. The only organ-related problem was my largest organ—my skin, all of it—on public display. My lock, which had served me well over the course of hundreds of trips to the gym, now rejected me. The ramifications of this rejection rivaled those of the night of my junior prom when Bobby De Luca dumped me. This may in fact be worse, given that I was only half-naked then. There had to be a mistake. Was it the right locker? I checked the number. Yes. Maybe I'm in the wrong section. Nope. My desperation was so great that I tried variations on the lock's combination even though I knew they were wrong. I'd just opened the damn thing not ten minutes ago!

Never was hardened steel so tenacious as it was at that moment, in that locker room. I can't explain it. The lock simply ceased to function. The only upside to standing like an idiot in a public locker room—naked and dripping as I was—is that I'm exposed to the natural process of evaporation. So, I had that going for me. For several minutes,

I cursed my lock. In the meantime, the aforementioned rift repaired itself and my previously private locker room reverted to a public locker room. I looked around to see if anyone had noticed me; everyone seemed blissfully unaware of my predicament, and if that wasn't torment enough, they were aptly clothed. Fuck me! As such, I felt disinclined to prance up to any of those ladies in nothing but my birthday suit to elicit their help. What I wouldn't have given for just one chatty-Cathy and her malignant mole. Which brings us back to the present; me, naked and cursing.

I feel my standards of hygiene begin to wane, to the point where I may solicit a stranger's fungus-infested towel when at long last a woman wearing a Gold's Gym uniform walks in pushing a bucket and mop.

Cue the Hallelujah Chorus!

Over the course of my forty-two years, I have prayed to many a saint, but as of this moment—I glance at the name embroidered on my savior's shirt—Sylvia is my new favorite. Cowering in the corner, I wave at Sylva. She looks at me, eyebrows raised as if to say: *What is that crazy white woman doing?* I can see that she's perplexed and who can blame her, really? I'm sure I come off a bit frazzled and a lot naked. I rattle off my situation. Sylvia looks at me and shrugs. "No hablo Inglés."

Even though she doesn't understand a word I'm saying, you would think that my predicament is self-explanatory. However, given the abundance of the aforementioned nudity, perhaps crazy white women are a common occurrence in this locker room.

Summoning some chutzpah (my ex is Jewish), I step toward her hoping to lead her to my obstinate lock, and yet she hesitates, so I recount my plight in Spanish. It's choppy, but understanding dawns on her face, and I flash back (perhaps a poor choice of words) to my high school Spanish classes and those endless sessions of verb conjugation and noun agreement drills. I say a silent prayer of gratitude to Sister Angelica Marie.

Sylvia nods and when she props her mop against the wall and leaves, relief washes over me. My elation deflates when she returns holding a pair of bolt cutters. Don't get me wrong, I'm near giddy to see the bolt cutters, but dismayed that she did not bring me a towel.

Things for which I'm grateful:

1) That despite a probable inclination to do so, Sylvia refrained from openly mocking me.

2) Good genes, mainly those that contribute to long hair.

3) Dark chocolate.

4) Black and Decker for their array of affordable tools, especially bolt cutters.

With bolt-cutters firmly in hand, I face my steely foe and a new realization sinks in. My locker is on the top row. In order to get the necessary leverage to cut the lock I'm forced to perch myself on the bench. As if things weren't awkward enough already.

If I may take a moment, dear friends, allow me to bestow some constructive criticism. Should you ever happen upon a dripping naked woman, might I suggest that *you* perform the lock-cutting task? The person you're helping will very much appreciate it, and let us not forget that by definition being nude connotes an inherent lack of proper protective gear.

In any case, I think we can all agree that my lat-flies have paid off because that lock gives up like French soldiers on the beaches of Normandy. With my belongings now freed, I waste no time dressing and exiting the gym. On the drive home I make a mental list of the gyms in my area. Obviously, I can't show my face at Gold's ever again.

Upon returning home, I go straight to the laundry room to exorcise the offending fungus from my ill-fated towel. I'm shocked to discover at the bottom of my gym bag is my lock. No, not the one I'd snipped, but *my* lock. I figure it went like this. In my state of heightened anxiety, after I quarantined my CDC-outbreak towel, I forgot to lock my locker. Another person must have used the locker next to mine and accidentally put her lock on my locker. Which leads me to this: to the woman whose lock I unwittingly vandalized, I either apologize and will gladly recoup your loss, or may Whitney Cummings assail you with an endless loop of *2 Broke Girls'* reruns.

DECRESCENDO

LOVE/LOSS POEM

Lorraine Jeffery

Blindness separates us from things but deafness separates
us from people. - Helen Keller

A baby's sigh from the crib could rouse her or tiny
feet's pit-a-pat. She turned at the buzzing

in the cedar tree, creek lapping, muffle of wind, thrum
of heartbeat, susurrus of the aspens and faint

whisper from the bramble. She relished
the robin's clear treble and rocked with
the pounding hooves of trumpet-mouthed music.
Then,

adagio, a sotto
voce world of Mason jars full
of vowels, only

AT FIRST GLANCE

a drizzle of consonants
and scarred syllables. Shimmering
understanding claws at bending

willows of sound, scratch
of fingernail words
and cacophony. Now

and then, haloed
clear, but mostly,

a tapioca of static
pianissimo. She
smiles and nods.

THE STRANGE VANISHING OF CHARLES PRESCOTT, BILLIONAIRE

SPECULATIVE FICTION

Johnny Worthen

THE AIR WAS LIKE WAVES of transparent bacon—sizzling, hot, and spitting—suspended above the horizon in writhing waves of illusion. Heat shimmers. Desert mirage. Distant images promising water, but he knew it was only heat.

Behind him the highway lay two hours back. Untravelled and windswept, traced back along his tire-tracks, it was invisible from here. Before him, across the expanse of sun-beaten tawny desert rose the Cane Mountains, a short, jagged line of exposed rock cutting through the sandy plain like a line of broken teeth. Lonely, out of place, dry and lifeless, yet the peaks swayed like living fronds in the heat's distortion. That's how she'd described it.

He tried to gauge the distance to the range—ten miles? Twenty? Five? It was impossible to tell through the phantasmic air. It was the wrong measurement anyway. The desert thinks in time not distance. A league could be a moment rushed down a flooded river; a mile a lifetime. Without roads even his new jeep would be hard pressed to make it there in half a day.

The Cane Mountains were much easier to approach from the other side where paved roads led up from Fosterville. Well-kept and better travelled, they lead directly to the heart of the Shimmer Load. Charles Prescott's mines. His mines: the Theresa, the Stranger and the Hot Damn, all producing 6% ore per ton and making him the richest man in the state, and in the top five for the country.

He hadn't stepped foot in this desert for over a decade, hadn't visited his concern since the new shaft was started eleven years back. There was no need. He had an army of engineers and managers to keep things running now. In the beginning though, he practically lived here, but that was long ago, sixty-six years to be precise.

He could feel the beginnings of a sunburn on his scalp. Mesh hats weren't to be trusted. He retreated to the jeep but lacking a destination, didn't get inside. Instead he found the narrow shade at the side and lowered himself into the sand, leaning against the door.

He smelled axel grease and heat, distant sage and heat, Danish cologne and heat. He watched the shimmers and strained sand through his fingers, pouring out the warm grains slowly in imitation of an hourglass. Tan puffs of dust poured out with it and lingered in the hot windless air. He remarked his hands, boney and splotched. Unadorned. Not even a watch. No rings. No ring.

Here it was, the maudlin mood he'd come here to revel in, for why else would he come here? This way? This season, if not to relive the moment?

And Theresa.

The name comes to him like a whisper of a forgotten prayer. The woman, not the mine, has been out of his life for so long, her name is like an ancient definition of a modern word. He can say it now and not think rock. He sees her face in his mind, a face he'd not seen for half a century clear and bright before him. It is this place, this light, heat and dry. And Theresa there under her faded green canvas hat, clear blue eyes, a clown white nose of zinc oxide over a laughing smile.

Theresa.

Theresa Maculry.

Was to be Theresa Maculry Prescott.

There's a hiss in the desert day. A high-pitched incessant sizzling siren he'd never been able to identify. It's always there in the hottest times, a hypersonic screech when the shimmers are most likely and the sun bears down like a press. He used to think it was insects, the noise. It might be, but he thinks now it's the scream of the ground itself, the superheating of sand to branding temperature, the rocks and oscillation, the mirage song.

The siren skipped for an instant. When it began again it was in another register, higher and hotter.

Distance moved.

The waves hiccoughed once, flickered, and burned again. Differently.

Prescott took off his sunglasses and squinted ahead. He wiped the sweat from his forehead and felt the starch of the new handkerchief across his brow. He dabbed his eyes with the rough cloth for want of anything better and returned his stare to the desert.

A shape appeared in the mirage; a shadow, a figure. A man walking toward him. He flashed in waves, broken and twisting as the light and heat distorted shape and size, making him look multiplexed and reassembling, huge and small, here and gone, but ever approaching.

Prescott remained against the jeep and watched him come, fanning himself with his expensive mesh hat.

After a time, the apparition was close enough to wave and held up a hand in greeting without breaking stride.

Prescott stood and raised his own hand.

He was not the same man as before. He laughed to think that it might have been.

"What's got your funny bone, mister?" said the stranger.

"I expected you to be someone else."

"God?"

"God?" said Prescott. "Why God?"

"They say God lives in the desert."

"Do you live in the desert?"

"No. I'm not God." He winked and extended his right hand. "I'm Fanuel. Like Manuel, but with an F. You could say my folks were fans of Manuel, but not enough to name me after him. Call me Fan. It's a cool name. Get it?" He smiled.

"I'm Charles Prescott." They shook hands.

Fanuel looked over the jeep and pointed to the new car sticker in the window. "Don't suppose you have any water to spare in that nice new jeep of yours?"

"I have."

Prescott opened the passenger door and dug a bottle of water out of the shrink-wrapped carton. He handed it to him.

"Designer brand water," said Fan. "Aren't I lucky. I don't suppose you have raspberry vanilla flavor?"

"I'm afraid I just—"

"Just joshing ya." Fanuel twisted open the bottle and downed the drink in one pull.

"Want another?"

"Don't mind if I do. I'll take one for later too, if it's alright. My canteen was getting a little sparse." He shook a dented aluminum flask and listened for the slosh.

Prescott passed him half a dozen bottles.

"Mighty generous of you," said Fan. "Mind if I join your shade for a spell?"

"Won't be here long, but you're welcome while it lasts."

Fanuel sat down.

Prescott noticed the man's worn jeans and beaten boots, wide-brimmed hat and creased face. He carried himself like a man in his late twenties but the sun had aged him so it was only a guess. He was timeless. His cheeks were sharp and crimson, his hair a tawny desert tan, his eyes the color of chocolate. His skin was the deep chestnut year-round sun and wind caress.

"You look like you live in the desert," said Prescott.

51

"And you look like you live in a penthouse in New York."

Prescott was taken aback. That's exactly where he lived now.

"I'm just on a little walk-about," said Fan opening another bottle of water and taking a measure sip. "I wander the desert to get things clear. Is that what you're doing?"

"I'm a little old to walk the desert."

Fan shrugged. "Why are you here then? Burying a body? Not mine I hope."

"I'm actually not sure why I'm here."

"Then you're in the right place."

"Are you hungry? I have some snacks." It occurred to Prescott that if he'd met Fan in New York, on the street or subway, anywhere, he'd not have given him the time of day let alone offered him food. He'd have had him arrested if he'd been on Prescott Enterprises property. Would have pressed charges if he'd as much as panhandled a dime in front of his building.

"I'm fine," said Fan. "Water is a real treat."

"I have plenty."

"Who'd you think I was?"

"What?"

Fan stretched his legs out and crossed them at the ankles. He tipped his hat up and gave Prescott an appraising look. "You said you thought I was someone else when I walked up. You were laughing about it. Now don't get me wrong, Charles, but you don't look like a man who laughs a lot."

"How would you know that?" Prescott spoke with returning authority, indignation in his voice. He let it remain.

"You face ain't accustomed to it," said Fan. "When you smiled, it looked like your cheeks had to cut new creases for it to be there. The frown ones, like those there—" He pointed to his chin. "Those are good and deep. Well used."

"I think I should be going." Prescott reached into his pocket for his keys.

"I'm just joshing you, Charles. Don't be so uptight. This is the desert. It's hot and it's stark and it's as clear as it can be down here. Who'd you think I was?"

Prescott glanced at the dancing mirage and thought to point to it as a counter example of Fan's clarity remark, but staring into the shimmers, he lost the urge to fight and took his hand out of his pocket.

"You're the second man I've seen come out of a mirage like that."

"Someone was here earlier?" asked Fan. "Overpopulation is becoming a real problem."

"Not today. It was years ago. Many years ago. Sixty-six years ago."

"Sixty-six years? You're dating yourself, Charles."

"I'm eighty-nine."

"Get out of here."

"Money can't make you immortal, but it's good for longevity."

"You're rich?"

Prescott nodded.

"A generous rich man? Who'd have thought?" said Fan raising his water bottle in salute. "Only in the desert."

"I wasn't born rich," said Prescott.

"No?"

"I made my money when I was your age."

Fan smiled.

"See those mountains there?"

Fan squinted across the plain through the mirage and nodded. "Hard to miss them, illusions and all."

"I was out here on a field trip for my graduate work."

"A doctor in philanthropy?" said Fan with a wink. "Handing out water?"

"Geology," said Prescott.

"Lucky you."

A bead of sweat raced down Prescott's neck and under his shirt. He shivered. He lowered himself beside Fan in the shade of the vehicle.

"It was easier then," said Prescott. "Looking back, that was the moment my life shifted from hopeful to bleak."

Prescott listened to the hiss, chasing thoughts and regrets and then started, suddenly remembering he wasn't alone. "Why am I telling you this?"

"There's truth in the desert," said Fan. "Sometimes you find it, sometimes you lose it. Sometimes you share. This is what the desert does."

"I thought you said God was in the desert."

"I did."

Prescott squinted at his companion and tried to read him. His face was dirty and sweat-creased with brow lines and laugh lines bespeaking an expressive countenance. It was hard and placid now.

"Those shimmers aren't truth," Prescott said pointing toward his mountain.

"Those are reflections." The authority in the man's voice surprised Prescott.

"I've heard of crazy men who walk the desert trying to find something. Hermits and peyote-stoned new-age seekers. Is that what you want to be?"

"Tell me about the other man," said Fan, his face still and waiting.

Hiss filled the air. A chirp of grasshopper, a rustle of a critter in a bush, a distant shadow of a solitary bird. The dancing mirage.

"I was engaged to a girl," he said. "She was everything to me. She'd signed on to be a professor's wife which at the time was all I wanted to be. We'd come out here as a kind of pre-honeymoon. She was a trooper. She was no fan of the sun. Light skinned and beautiful, in the day, she hid under sunscreen, long-sleeved shirts— and straw hats, but at night, naked, under the moonlight on this plain, she glowed like life itself."

He felt new moisture on his face and was surprised to find a tear running down his cheek.

"The man approached just as you did. Just kind of materialized out of the mirage one afternoon and walked into camp."

"Is this where your camp was?"

"Near here, but I don't think this is the exact spot. It might be but it doesn't feel like it."

"Time changes things."

"I can't believe I'm telling you this."

"It's okay, Charles. This is the desert and things are different here. Clear. Time is relative. Mirrors and illusions and promises and stone—this is the raw canvas of creation."

"Sure you're not a new-age hippie?"

"No." His face became again a display of expression as he leaned back and grinned.

"He was an old man," said Prescott. "Like you he was desert beaten and dirty."

"I wear my dust with pride."

"So did he. My fiancé was afraid of him. She called me over from an arroyo where I was doing a stratum check. I crested the ravine and saw him standing just outside the camp. He looked ancient. His clothes were different. I invited him to come forward. I offered him water, but he refused to come a step closer."

Fan nodded as if he understood, but what it was his companion could gather from that, Prescott couldn't imagine.

"'What do you want?' I asked him."

"'What do *you* want?' was his smart-ass reply."

"'I want to be rich,' I said. I just blurted it out. Like it was the punchline for a joke. The standard answer for a college kid facing student loans."

"That's what everyone thinks they want," said Fan. "We'd be hard put to find anyone who doesn't want to be rich."

"I remember how strange it was. Surreal. Magical."

"The desert. ."

"I remember thinking that I really should give him a better answer, that here was my genie and I shouldn't screw this up. I thought to correct myself even then. I remember seeing my fiancé, still scared, standing behind me as if asking me to protect her from a great and terrible threat. I should have thought of her. I should have changed my answer to. . to something else, but I didn't. I didn't. I left it at that."

Fan's face was again implacable and still. Prescott faced the mirage again.

"The stranger pointed to the Canes over there. 'There's a canyon in those mountains, a V-shaped shit of a canyon. You'll need ropes. Climb up a quarter mile to a flood basin and look for the tell-tale quartz.'"

"Quartz?"

"Gold is associated with quartz," said Prescott. "I knew what he was telling me as he said it. I knew its significance."

"Of course," said Fan. "What then?"

"I offered the man water again and food. Shelter. I even asked him his name, but he wouldn't say anything else. I took a step toward him and he waved me off. Told me to be still, not to follow him. Then he turned around and walked back into the mirage. I never saw him again."

"You went to the mountain and checked?"

"The next day. It was just as he said. Quartz deposit and flood run off. We found nuggets in the puddle. It was wonderful."

"It was?"

Prescott closed his eyes. "For a while."

"It cost you," said Fan. It wasn't a question, but a flat statement.

"It all happened so fast. I had it staked within a week, claimed and filed in two. Core samples in a month and twenty million in backers by the end of the year. It was like an avalanche. It was hard to keep up. Once the mines started producing, it got worse. IPO, investors, board, money, backstabs, audits, bribes, bureaucratic fights, shady connections, toxic dumps. Everyone wanting something. I was cornered. Every year I had to fight to keep it, I had to fight back, fight hard. Everyone was against me. Everyone wanted something. If I didn't stay vigilant, prepare for the theft, I'd have been ruined. I nearly was several times. It was a full-time job. Being rich is hard."

"I've heard that," Fan said.

"You have?"

"No."

"I never got married, not to her—the one who was with me then. I married instead three snakes who each cheated on me."

"But you cheated on them."

"In self-defense," said Prescott before realizing how stupid it sounded.

The conversation ceased, and the hiss seemed to rise in volume.

Prescott half-whispered, "It was not at all what I thought it would be."

"Being rich?"

"My life," he said. "My life is measured by the day the

stranger came into my camp; before and after. Poor, rich; happy, miserable."

"Money can't buy happiness, but I'm told it can rent it."

"You ever hear anyone say on their deathbed that they wished they'd made money?"

"Once or twice," said Fan. "But they were fools."

"Fools. Fool's gold." Prescott laughed.

"You're dying."

"You can't be as old as me and not be falling apart."

"Eighty-nine is a good long life."

"Long, but not good. It was good before. . It was good before."

The sun crept over the jeep, removing their shade by inches. Fan's legs were in the sun; his waist and torso shaded still, for a little while more.

"You can't blame yourself," said Fan. "You were young. The young make mistakes. It's what they do. I blame the stranger."

"The stranger? Why?"

"You said he was old. He should have been smarter than you at that age. Wiser. He shouldn't have made you rich. He should have given you something more valuable."

"More valuable than the richest mine in modern American history?"

"Yes."

"Like what?"

Fan's lips curled up in a little smile and he shook his head almost sorrowfully. "I've got to get going," he said.

"What?" said Prescott. "In the hottest part of the day."

"Walk-about," he said. "I thank you for your generosity."

"It's the desert," said Prescott getting up heavily. Fan didn't move to help him. "If we'd have met in Manhattan—"

"You'd have had me arrested," supplied Fan.

"Yeah."

"So long, Charles Prescott."

"Wait where are you going?"

He pointed into the far distance.

"Not that way? Not back into the mirage?"

He shook his head. "That's not my way," he said.

Prescott held open his hands as if reaching into the air for a question to keep him, an answer to a riddle. "Thanks for listening," he said.

"I would have liked to have met Theresa," Fanuel said.

"Yes. She died a while ago. Car accident in Montana. But we were broken up by then. I found out about it years later."

"Still."

"Yeah."

And with that Fanuel walked away into the desert. Prescott watched him go until distance and an arroyo hid him from view.

He turned and looked at the mirage, remembering again the stranger who'd entered his camp, wondering what he might have said that would have turned his life differently. He'd been dressed queerly, he remembered. Dirty and sweaty, and dust covered, in a blue short-sleeved shirt with creases as if freshly ironed. His jeans were new and bright blue beneath the spattered dust. His boots unworn and of a kind he'd never seen before. His hat, a strange mesh thing that let too much sun through. He glanced down at his own clothes, seeing them for the first time. Again.

His breathing caught in his throat and he felt a need for a heart pill.

"I never mentioned her name," he said into the heat. "I never told him Theresa's name."

The shimmers shook and swayed and danced before him like hope. He put on his hat and took aim at the mirage. He marched forward. Each step hurt his joints, raced his heart and warmed him with purpose. The sand was deep and fought him, but onward he trudged, kicking up dust that followed him and choked him and settled in slow motion, talcum, heat-soaked, and slow.

Time is different in the desert.

LOVE IS THE DISTANCE BETWEEN US

Short Fiction

Britney Johnson

WE SIT SIDE BY SIDE at the conference table. Our pinkies close but never touching. You look at her the way that I look at you. The clock ticks with every second. I wait. She does not love you. Can't you see? It is me, only me. The meeting drones on. Our coworkers around the room have glazed eyes. Numbers and projections fill your screen as you take notes with efficiency, never looking down at the keyboard. I notice. I notice, and she does not. The watch checking begins as five o'clock rolls around. You glance at her as I watch you. The meeting ends, and she is looking at her phone, not at you. A smile plays on her face, a text from a boy perhaps. She can't see the man in front of her. She hurries away because she does not care. Oh but I do. I do. Notice me. Notice me.

You look for her, but she is gone. Gone, can't you see? You try to follow, but I stop you with, "Good evening."

"You too," you say, and though it looks to others like just a brush-off, I know better. I can hear the church bells ringing.

You leave the same way you always do. Going to your car that is always in the same spot. You are dependable, predictable. It makes you easy to follow.

Two cars behind, always. A girl has to play hard-to-get, you know. The lights are timed to a rhythm we move to. Go and stop at every light. As you race to the next, I hear your engine race and purr. You want me to know that you're a man's man, but I already know it.

We part ways, but only for a moment, my sweet. Did you know I bought the house behind you? It has great windows just like yours does. Of course, my windows have curtains. A girl needs her privacy. But you want me to see you. As you jog, droplets of sweat move down the curves in your muscles. I brush my lips with my finger. Oh to kiss. To kiss you would be heaven.

You move your feet, dragging after your long exercise. I see your silhouette in the ghosted window of your bathroom as you remove the rest of your clothing. This one detail of your life you keep from me. Yes one tiny thing, but I can't help but feel that you are farther from me now. Only a shadow. So I move from watching to preparing myself for the night. Perfect hair and my tight silk nightgown. You would love it. You will love it. Once we are married you can build me a fence around the house we will share, but for now, I am glad no barriers stand between us.

My bare feet on the lawn you perfectly manicure for me. I open the small door to the crawl space below your house and make my way to my sleeping bag below your room. I blow you a kiss. Dream of me, not her. You wouldn't want me getting jealous again.

I thought after the last girl, you would have learned; I am the only one. The only one who loves you.

NEVER FORGET

LOVE/LOSS POEM

Denis Feehan

In the twenty-second century
The kids all fly to school
The teacher is a hologram
Who is sitting on a stool
And she's teaching all the students that
In nineteen forty-one
The Zeroes sank our battleships
In the Sunday rising sun

And then every year the nation mourned
The men who died that day
The TV showed us long parades
And Pastors all would pray
But these students have no memory
Of Japanese attacks
They cannot feel the shock and fear
They only know the facts

AT FIRST GLANCE

No, the students of this century
Feel nothing in their breast
They're simply memorizing dates
To pass this Friday's test
And then Monday when the hologram
Is teaching history
She'll tell of New York City when
It fell upon one knee
All the students will see video
When twins were torn apart
By Arabs aiming stolen planes
Directly at their heart

Now for homework they must all create
An image of that town
When evil brought it smoke and fire
And the towers both came down
And they'll do their best to get an "A"
By representing fear
But though they'll show the scene so well
They will not shed a tear

But that's just the way it is my friends
Don't blame the youth at all
They learn of long forgotten days
Then head off to the mall
So the seventh of December and
That sad September day
Will never be forgotten but
Remembered? No, no way.

CHRISTMAS COOKIE...
OOH LA LA!

Humor

James Beers

As far back as I can remember my family has decorated our Christmas trees with frosted sugar cookies
and cellophane-wrapped popcorn balls. It's a tradition
that stems from my parents' first Christmas together in
the 1960s. Back then my parents were so poor that they
couldn't afford a tree or decorations. At the time, Dad
was in college studying zoology and Mom worked part-
time as a cashier at Sears. To make ends meet, Dad took
up sewing machine repair under the tutelage of an old
blind lady.

Listening to them talk about it, you'd think the story
came straight from Dickens or O. Henry, but only the
part about being poor at Christmas. The story changed
tone a few minutes in when Dad said, "That was back in
our lawless days."

For their first tree, my parents, under the cover of night's darkness, pilfered a scraggly, midget-sized spruce from the nearby city park. Wearing a ski mask, Dad cut down the tree with a hand saw and then he stuffed the tree into the getaway car, a beat-up Dodge Dart driven by my lead-footed mother.

Partly to mask their larceny and partly to bring some holiday spirit to their apartment, they shrouded the tree in homemade decorations. Mom managed to scrape together enough ingredients from their cupboards to make a few dozen sugar cookies and popcorn balls, which she hung from the spruce's boughs with paperclips. Dad made paper chains from graded homework, careful not to include his professors' marks on any of the links so as not to squelch the Christmas spirit of generosity and good nature.

Not only did the decorated tree deliver Christmas cheer, it also provided snacks and a couple of meals between mid-December and New Year's.

"What's for dinner tonight, my lead-footed lady?"

"Why, sugar cookie topped with popcorn ball, my masked man."

After Dad graduated from college and established employment, my parents found the funds to add frosting to the cookies and food coloring to the popcorn balls. Seven years after their first Christmas, I debuted as a long, big-headed baby in the middle of December, effectively setting the date for future cookie decorating shindigs.

Every year on my birthday, the cookie-decorating tradition grew both in size and as an art form. Sprinkles of all sorts, Red Hots, chocolate chips, and those little silver BBs you're not supposed to eat accumulated with each December. Tweezers, toothpicks, bobby pins, sewing needles, and floss came in as tools for detail work in the frosting medium.

But what grew most emphatically was an informal competition for the best-decorated cookie. Nobody ever said anything about any decorating tournament, there were no prizes or designated places on the tree for special cookies, nor did Dad or Mom open the event with, "welcome to our annual decorating contest." We just inherently knew it was a beauty pageant for decorated sugar cookies.

The competition didn't start or get too heated until my siblings and I graduated from the abstract art phase back in the 1980s. It's pretty easy to spot the transition in family photographs. Cookies before that time period resembled globby imitations of Jackson Pollock paintings, complete with the mixed colors of several frostings and sprinkles, but with even less appeal and market value.

I remember well the birthday—my twelfth—when my sister threw down the gauntlet. It started innocently enough; a single snide comment about the appearance of my tree-shaped cookie.

"That doesn't look much like a Christmas tree. The trunk's frosted blue," Mindy said. I might have ignored such a remark any other time, but the guys I'd invited had overheard and were peering over my shoulder, snickering.

"Oh yeah?" I said, pointing at Mindy's star cookie. "Well, stars aren't blue either."

"Actually—" Russell tried to pipe in over my left shoulder before I elbowed him in the gut. Russell was the human equivalent of a college science curriculum. Surely he had some factoid about blue stars.

My star looks better than your tree," Mindy responded.

"We'll see about that," I said, opening up the first family cookie decorating challenge.

Determined to create a decorated masterpiece the heavens would smile upon, I grabbed a fresh cookie—a snowman—sat down at the kitchen table, and went to work. I was frosting the snowman white, paying careful attention to keep the frosting from escaping the cookie edge, when my friend Dean whispered to me.

"Trunks are brown, dude."

"I know they're brown, bonehead," I whispered back. "Do you see any brown frosting?"

"Yeah, right there," he said, pointing to our friend Crooney's cookie. Rusty Crooney had decorated a Christmas tree cookie that would give Santa Claus a double take. It had a brown frosting trunk textured exactly like tree bark. Crooney had left the cookie on a paper plate and Dean and I moved closer to examine his handiwork.

"Looks like he mixed frosting colors to make brown," Dean said, noting the brown frosting smear near the edge of the paper plate.

"Yeah. I'll bet Crooney's got a painting pallet for frosting back home," I said. Then, feeling jealous, I grabbed the cookie, broke it in half, stuffed one half into Dean's gawking mouth, and shoved the other half into my own mouth. As I munched on the cookie, I held my finger up to my lips and gave Dean the "you be quiet or else" sign.

"One of you guys ate my cookie because it was better than yours," Crooney said later that night, shaking his frosting knife at us. He suspected Dean had eaten it, given the dabs of green frosting Dean hadn't licked from the corners of his mouth. For the rest of the night he never took his eyes off any of his other creations. "Well, never again!"

Lucky for me, Crooney's vigilance seemed to stunt his creativity; afterward he couldn't even frost a decent Christmas globe. Instead, he kept waving his knife at anyone who came within arm's length of his workstation. But unlucky for me, his suspicion spread and I wasn't able to eliminate any other competition. Russell snarled over his cookies, guarding them like a Doberman. Dean resorted to licking his workmanship, leaving behind healthy layers of slobber. Mindy escaped to her room to decorate behind a closed door.

The only other opponents—my parents and younger brother, Adam—weren't threats. My parents had grown bland in their advancing years (a factor reflected in their decorating) and Adam was still working in unrefined dabs and globs and coating all frosting in sporadic, unpatterned sprinkles.

When the evening was over, my snowman cookie—a chocolate chip-buttoned, carrot-nosed, scarf-wearing, top-hatted tour de force—garnered *oohs* and *aahs* and several handshakes and high-fives of admiration. Mindy's pink-winged angel only took home the obligatory parent comment, "yes, that cookie's very nice, dear." Russell made a nice rocket out of a tree, but he clearly missed the Christmas theme. Dean's cookies were too slimy. And Crooney, who got so nervous guarding his workstation, devoured his half dozen Christmas globes in a bout of stress eating.

Clearly, I had won, and Mindy was fuming.

"Just wait 'til next year," Mindy said. "You'll have to do better than that ugly snowman."

"Oh yeah," I said. "You better bring your game, Pink Wings."

The Christmas cookie art war had begun.

Vital, unspoken rules were set up and strategies developed during that first Christmas cookie showdown. I spell out those rules and strategies here to set the stage for what happened at a family Christmas cookie decorating shindig almost twenty years later.

Rule #1: The theme is Christmas. Stray from that theme at your own expense.

Rule #2: Stick to the decorating supplies provided. Shame on you if you use unauthorized materials and tools.

Rule #3: Dirty, underhanded behaviors—using up sprinkles or a certain color of frosting, "accidentally" eating someone else's cookie, "accidentally" bumping someone else's cookie so it falls on the ground, etc.—are allowed. Go too far though and suffer the consequences.

Strategy #1: Protect your cookies at all costs, never let them out of your sight. Often referred to as Crooneying Your Cookie.

Strategy #2: Eat any competition that poses a threat. But be sure to lick your lips and destroy any evidence of your crime so as to avoid the Dean Folly.

It's a cutthroat affair, not for the faint of heart.

When my parents heard that my wife Jenna, our one-year-old son Joseph, and I would like to spend Christmas with them in 2007, my mom declared that she would postpone the annual December 15th cookie decorating until Christmas Eve.

Ooh, something to look forward to.

Truth be told, however, I was a bit rusty and my decorating skills were lax. Since leaving the nest I'd decorated cookies only two times and both times I'd frosted in haste and applied sprinkles with reckless abandon. It was ugly. So were the cookies. But I've never known a cookie art piece to taste any better than a shoddy glob job.

Jenna was somewhat familiar with our cookie tradition as we'd decorated a batch with friends the year
before. However, I had not introduced the concept of
best cookie and she knew nothing of that revered quest
or its nuances. What was the worst that could happen?
She doesn't win and she sees a little bit of sibling rivalry?
No big deal.

After dinner on Christmas Eve, Mom pulled out the
tub of four dozen sugar cookies and set them on the bar in
the kitchen. On the sly, I scoped out the competitors—my
parents, my two youngest teenage sisters, and my wife.
Piece of cake.

From the pantry, Dad carried in seven bowls of different colored frosting and a box brimming with sprinkles,
Red Hots, and chocolate chips. My hands tingled anx-
iously. Visions of blonde-haired, angel cookies, wings and
bodies frosted white and trimmed with silver BB sprinkles
danced around on the back of my eyeballs. I licked my
lips in anticipation. The clang of butter knives on the table
went off in my head like a boxing ring bell and I came out
swinging. If I sank any further into the zone, I'd drown in
my own creativity and sugar cookie couture.

Oblivious to the other wannabe decorators, I pushed
my way through to the bar.

"I'll take that, that, that, and that," I said, reaching for
a tree, an angel, a star, and a snowman cookie.

"Take it easy, Jim," my sister Kerry said. "It's not like
this is a competition."

I stared at her with my game face. Just keep thinking that, cookie rookie. "Give me the white and yellow," I said, still eyeing Kerry, "and do not disturb."

From the corner of my eye, I caught Jenna glaring at me, something furrowing her brow. Suspicion? Visual reprimand? No way she knew about the best cookie. Still glaring at me, she took an angel cookie and the bowl of purple frosting and stowed herself at the corner of the bar.

"Mom?" Jenna said. "What kind of cookie decorations are you looking for?"

"Oh, anything you'd like," Mom responded. "Be creative, have fun."

What? Be creative? Are you trying to give her hints?

As I poured my inner artist into a Rockefeller Center Christmas tree lookalike, Mom and Dad began the ritual telling of their first Christmas. While everyone else was caught up in the story, I paused for a second to peruse the contending works-in-progress. Kerry and Kimi were into the glam look, slathering their cookies in pink and purple and dousing the frosting in thick layers of sprinkles and silver BBs. Mom and Dad decorated in the same humdrum two- and three-tone motifs they had practiced for years. Jenna slaved over what looked like a purple angel. How she could listen and at the same time work details with a toothpick, I'll never know.

Soon I had a menagerie of cookie masterpieces—a Christmas tree that would put Crooney's to shame, an angel straight from the Bible, a snowman from a Currier & Ives scene, and a star the spitting image of the original that shone over Bethlehem. I was a little disappointed with the angel's sandals but only refined eyes would see the dissymmetry in the straps.

Not too shabby for a rusty cookie artist.

Before anyone could scrutinize my entries, I put them on a paper plate and hid them in the loaded, rollaway dishwasher. No one would look there. At about the same time, Mom hauled the fudge and toffee out of the freezer, and the rest of the gang evacuated the bar.

And their cookies.

"Time to eliminate the competition," I whispered to myself, rubbing my hands together like all evil villains do before committing crimes.

Kimi had created a decent Christmas globe, which I devoured in three bites. Kerry's glam Santa Claus was a fair, contending entry, but the frosting was a bit thick for my liking and I thought the excess sugar crystal sprinkles might thrust me into a diabetic coma. So I "accidentally" bumped it onto the floor and Santa's glam head fell off.

"Ooops," I whispered, and then laughed a low-volume cackle.

I made my way around the bar, scarfing down two of my dad's stars and one of my mom's bells. When I came to Jenna's single entry I faltered and grabbed the edge of the bar to steady myself. Before my eyes lay a purple angel that had been decorated, it appeared, by a studied and seasoned painter of nudes. Certain parts of the angel's upper half were anatomically correct. And I don't mean in the Renaissance-age, cherubic sense of angel artistry.

"What is this?!" I said, gasping with shock and surprise.

Jenna must have seen that I was studying her cookie, for the next thing I knew, she was standing beside me.

"It's a monster," she said. "See? Here are its ears, here's its mouth, and here are its eyes—" she continued, pointing lastly at the angel's bosomy chest.

"A monster?" I interrupted. "It looks more like a half-naked angel!" Jenna's face went pale as recognition set in.

"Oh no," she said, bringing her hands to each side of her face. "I wasn't even thinking about that. I was trying to be creative."

"Well," I said, "that's one way to do it."

My poor innocent wife had actually seen a monster in the angel cookie, kind of like Michelangelo saw a naked man in that piece of marble. I would've eaten the cookie to spare Jenna any more embarrassment, but I couldn't bring myself to do it. It just felt kind of like eating pornography. I suggested that we get rid of it and was about to reach for it and do so when my mom came by and glimpsed the cookie.

"What is that?" She pointed at the cookie. She didn't see a monster either.

I was quick to the punch, responding, "Jenna did it." I couldn't have my own mother thinking I would make such a thing.

"It's supposed to be a monster," Jenna said, the color of her face changing from ghost white to tomato red.

"A monster?" Mom responded. "It looks more like a half-naked angel!" That's when Dad, hearing all the commotion at the bar, came over to see what was up.

"What's going on over—ooh!" he said as he approached and saw the cookie.

"It's Jenna's," I said. She elbowed me in the side. I was about to explain that the cookie was supposed to be a monster, but Dad let out a half-stifled chuckle and was trying to restrain a full-blown laugh. The hilarity of the situation hit me as well and I chuckled too. Soon Dad and I were laughing and Mom was chuckling alongside us. Jenna clearly found it difficult to see the humor. From the color of her face and the display of her sheepish demeanor, I'd guess she was mortified. Call it a hunch.

Before we laughers could get too raucous, Mom shushed us. "Shhh! We can't let the kids see this, and we definitely can't hang it on the tree. Jim, you eat it."

"I...don't feel comfortable doing that," I said.

"Beers, you eat it then," Mom said to Dad.

"That seems kind of..dirty," Dad responded.

"We can just throw it away," Jenna suggested.

"Wait! I have a better idea," Mom said. "Let's give it to the Fluhmans." At first, I wondered why on earth she would give a naked angel cookie to anyone; it's just not one of those things that you gift. But evidently, the Fluhmans, a newlywed couple my parents knew well, had some kind of honeymoon tree over at their place, and my mom thought the angel cookie would make a great addition. Weird to say the least. Nonetheless, Mom took the cookie over to the Fluhmans.

With the excitement of Jenna's unique cookie art, I had forgotten all about my own creative pieces and, when

I went to the kitchen to retrieve them and hang them on the tree, I saw that somebody had started the dishwasher.

"NO!" I yelled and then opened the dishwasher door. But it was too late, my cookies had all but disintegrated. The only thing left were a few fragments of droopy paper plate clinging to the upper dishrack and some half-dissolved sprinkles flecking the dishes. The 2007 battle for best cookie was over. The winner? A tossup between a Pepsi symbol Christmas globe by Dad and Kerry's headless glam Santa Claus.

Although the Christmas cookie decorating tradition still lives on every December, after the naked angel, the best cookie contest has lost most of its pizzazz. And another thing? Jenna has yet to decorate another angel cookie. In fact, you won't find any angel cookies on our trees anymore. Jenna got rid of the angel cookie cutter as soon as we returned home from Christmas 2007.

MY UNCLE

PROSE POEM

Neil Dabb

A poet passed
A writer died.
A philosopher magnifique.
Prepare a place on the other side.
And endless vistas behold.
Observe the view for a limitless story.
And step aside as all the writers combine.
To tell the story.
Create a scene.
For those who are left behind.
And send the verse on the endless winds.
With charts for brains
And wings of light.
His words will homeward fly.
For those who've passed.
And those to come.
And loved ones left behind.

BLESSED BY THE LAYING
ON OF WINGS

SPIRITUAL ESSAY

Shirley Manning

THE NIGHT OF LAUREN'S AND Nick's wedding, we stayed at the University Inn, on the campus of Utah State University. After a restful sleep, I went out on a walk in the old, stately part of campus. It was a pristine morning – spring in full swing, sun warming my shoulders, flower-fragrant air waking my senses. The crystal-blue sky drew my eyes to heights I couldn't see, but I felt I was peering at Heaven.

My mind was at rest and my emotions peaceful, after the joyful (if not stressful) tension of planning, preparing and experiencing the momentous day of the wedding and celebration that followed.

I became more and more delighted with the beauty of the day, as I walked along vacant paths abandoned by hundreds of students who had already fled to their summer lives. I shared the solitude with flitting, singing birds that crisscrossed in the air to perch momentarily in the high branches of a pine-tree cathedral. A squirrel dashed across the grass and zipped up one of the giant trees, scolding me for frightening him.

My mind was quiet, only taking in what I felt happening around me. Everything in my field of perception seemed to be directing my attention skyward. I heard a faint whoosh of wings coming from behind me, before I could turn to see the crow. He swooped precisely through my hair without touching my head, then soared confidently beyond me and rose gradually out of sight.

This was not a menacing gesture from a heckling bird, dismissing me from his territory. But he certainly had my attention. Maybe there was a message for me mailed par avion.

Maybe the beautiful feeling that came to me when the bird gently brushed my hair was to remind me that others who love us, who live beyond our sight, had been with us at the wedding – and that I had completely missed them. Had I been so grounded and focused on the proceedings of the day that I had not understood the eternal implications of joining a man and a woman and their families?

I believe that I had excluded from my vision the ethereal wedding guests who were certainly present. And through some mercy, of which I feel unworthy, a more inclusive vision of the occasion had been delivered to me by the wings of a crow.

cc: Wesley James Manning, Don and Ruth Wood, Zona Larsen, Jenny Belliston, Sidney LaMar Manning, and other angels.

TWO STEPS FROM YOU

LOVE/LOSS POEM

Britney Johnson

Two steps I can never take.
For the dreams of this moment will never change.
The silence that lingered will never leave
for the words that I wanted from you will never be spoken.
"I love you," I called, and you stopped.
What went through your mind?
Why didn't you say it back?
Would two more steps have saved your life.
A hug, a kiss?
What would have stopped you?
What could have stopped you?
You fired a gun.
You should have stayed.
You should have lived.
Even though I call another Mom, you will always be my
mother, and I will always love you.

HOMEMADE BREAD

CREATIVE NONFICTION

Sara Mortensen

BENEATH THE PAPER SHEATH, THE blade of my grand-mother's bread knife is untarnished. However, the paper is stained near the seam, a sick and tormented shade of amber bordered with a fine-lined cobalt pattern like jaundiced Chinese porcelain. "Lifetime Guarantee" is stamped in the center with bold, serif font, reminiscent of ads from the 1940s. I am not sure how old this knife truly is, but I am surprised that decades of sheathing and unsheathing have not severed the paper in half.

The handle is black plastic textured with microscopic goosebumps. Though it feels cheap, it too is remark-ably intact. No scrapes, no burn marks, no chips in its light and delicate surface. I hold it firmly in my hand, wrapping my fingers around its coarse shell. I imagine my grandma's palm pressing into mine, her blood pulsing through the knife, her goosebumps chilling my skin.

Carefully removing the paper cover, I observe the blade's serrated edge. The knife's teeth alter lengths in no discernable pattern, like rippling waves in a cold and unpredictable ocean. The point of the knife is pronged and sharp. Neptune's trident.

Grazing my fingers along the knife's edge, I feel the blade is still sharp though I myself have never sharpened it; I wonder if decades of carving through homemade loaves of bread had maintained its bite and polish. Even looking at it brings to mind the heavenly aroma of yeast and flour mixed with stale cigarettes wafting through my grandparents' former home.

When I was a child, my grandparents always prepared a fresh loaf of bread before guests arrived. My grandpa would make the bread and my grandma would cut it into slices and toast it for her grandchildren. Though she didn't do anything particularly uncommon, my cousins and I all maintain that she made the best toast. Perhaps it was the ceremony of it. As my grandpa chain-smoked in the kitchen and watched *The Joy of Painting with Bob Ross* in his chair, hovering just two inches from the television screen, she would slather a freshly toasted slice of bread in butter and cut it into four soldiers before serving it to us on a small, child-size plate. We, as children, would gobble it up, licking drips of melted butter from our fingertips, blissfully unaware of the cancerous smoke looming over our heads, a decade of ceremony settling slowly in my grandma's chest.

Years later, our parents would tell us she has lung cancer. It started slow, and then it consumed her all at once. In her final days, she would lie in her dim-lit guest bedroom—unable to make it up to her own sunny bed in the upstairs loft. She lives alone, without care and companionship after my grandpa's passing more than ten years earlier. The home that had once smelled of bread and cookies became both sickly and sterile. We could feel cancer in the room like a haunting, a ghost that demanded to be acknowledged. And though some say adults aren't afraid of things like ghosts and monsters under the bed, we were all mortified. The ghost scared the grandchildren, and soon they stopped visiting altogether.

I remember my last visit when I was eighteen. I held her hand in mine, her skin white and delicate as wet paper, and kept her company as my mother prepared her a piece of toast. My grandma was having trouble eating, and it seemed everything no matter how mild or bland was too much to keep down. We helped prop her up in the bed and watched, helpless, as she nibbled on a stick of toast, trying hard to keep the crumbs from falling into the sheets. She didn't talk much, and neither did I. I just held her hand, gripping tighter and tighter as I stifled tears in the never-ending silence.

The next week was New Year's and I had a vacation planned. My mother begged me not to go, but it seemed, at least for a moment, that my grandma's health was improving. She was finally eating again, and color was beginning to return to her pallid skin. I took this grain of hope with me as I left town. I had spent months confronting death, and exhausted, I went searching for some escape.

I never got the call. I just came home to a family in mourning. We had lost her on New Year's Day, an unfortunate memory that resurfaces for all of us each year as the world is caught up in celebration. The wound is fresh, even years later, for how do you cauterize a wound that is severed anew by the pop of champagne bottles and the banging of pots and pans?

I realize now that I've never fully understood mortality or been able to cope with loss. It's not something people think to teach children, to prepare them for what is to come. The death of a family pet only teaches us that death exists. But we fight back by getting a new puppy the next day and the pain disappears like it was never there at all. In life, you cannot replace your loved ones. So, we must find comfort in the temporary and the uncertain, or let death consume us as well.

I put my nose close to the blade, hoping to detect even the faintest scent of bread and butter, but the smell is long gone.

I take the blade to the crust of my first loaf of homemade bread. Steam rises as I gently saw off a thick slice. I dip the forked tip of the knife into butter and coat the soft center of the bread, careful not to tear up the surface as the rigid teeth glide across it. I don't cut this slice into soldiers. Some things need to remain whole.

THE CARETAKER OF WOE'S GARDEN

Prose Poem

C.H. Hung

One lonely day
I wandered into a garden
Of dead weeds and roses
My mind blank
Eyes unseeing and
Thoughts tumbling but with
Nothing to say

It almost seemed
Out of place
The joyful song of birds
And cloudless blue sky
When inside
All I could do
Was cry

Tears and Sorrow
Were commonplace
A frequent visitor
Without Happiness's grace
A saddened spirit
Lived in Woe's garden
Created by our Maker
And I –
I was the garden's caretaker.

KNIFE FIGHT

Short Fiction

Anna Marasco

THE CARNIVAL CANDLES CAST GLOWS, bleeding shadows under the stars scratched in the New Mexican sky like large-grained salt scattered across a blackboard. I tickled the knife's blade with my slender fingertips and the audience hushed like they always did, as if they had never before seen a ten-year-old throw knives at her father. His narrow frame was tucked tightly against the poorly painted plywood backdrop, a red balloon clenched in his yellowed teeth that had widened to a snaggletoothed smile. I had already popped half a dozen balloons and my knives pinned the splattered remnants to the splintered wood. I had done my usual routine, starting at the toe and working my way up his smudged and raggedly clothed body to the final unpopped balloon. I didn't know what disgusted me more: my father, or the fact that I looked like him, complete to the freckles and frizzy orange mane, often mistaken as a clown's wig. We were carnies, after all.

I had been a carny since inside my mother's womb. My mother, eight months pregnant, would pose against the newly painted plywood backdrop in lace and tassels as my father's target. When he was sober, the show was executed perfectly. When he was drinking, however, he insisted on throwing the knives as close to her skin as possible, slicing the sides of her bulged belly, leaving scars etched in her flesh like feral cat claws. My parents tried to pass them off as brutal stretch marks.

After I was born, when most babies would learn to walk, talk, and taste the soil samples in their grandparents' backyards, I was standing for target practice. At two, I was the youngest knife thrower in carnival history. But even that prestige wasn't enough to keep my mother's attention. She didn't want to be a mother. She wanted to be a vaudeville star, devoid of stretch marks and petite pudding handprints on her silk pleated dresses. She left us: me, my father, and my little sister. I resented her for leaving my sister and me with our father, but I found solace later, looking back, in the fact that vaudeville was a vanishing act. Its stars like Buster Keaton and Fatty Arbuckle abandoned it and were making moving pictures. I liked to sneak into their movies at the local theatre, and escape, even just momentarily, from our family freak show with two shows and ten hours of practice daily.

I raised the knife in front of my face and squinted my focus to the final red balloon, smoothing my pink unitard, its brightness pale and faded like the backdrop's paint. I wanted to wear a tutu like a ballerina; a pink one with sparkles. The other knife throwers and carnival acts had fancy costumes with sequins and pearls. He made me wear long pants and long sleeves, to hide the bruises and bite marks. I clamped my legs together, the nightmarish memories always spun in my mind like one of the carnival's cheap rides. The nightly ritual of him rubbing the knives' handles all over my body, *in* my body, was carved in my skin and every morning I would boil the knives over the dwindling fire outside of our red gypsy caravan. No matter how long or how hot I boiled them, they never felt clean enough. I never felt clean enough.

I pointed the blade's tip at the target. I had to be perfect. Like always. I couldn't miss the shot. I missed once when I was six; that's when it started. The first bite mark on my inner thigh, the first time my dad made me wear long wool dresses in the desert's burning summer heat. That's when mother left. I figured it was my fault. It was my fault because I missed my target.

I extended my arm, knife in hand, to line up the target shot. Today had been the hottest day of the year and the sweat sank sticky in my skin. Today was the first time our father dressed my six-year-old sister in a long wool dress. Her sweat was dribbling, pooling in a puddle, like urine, on the ground between her legs.

I threw the knife and, like always, I heard the audience gasp as the blade whirled through the air. Except, this last knife fluttered like it was caught in a strong headwind. Its momentum slowed as it approached the target. Its silver glinted against the carnival candles' flickers before hitting its mark, catching my father's stubbled neck with the double-edge blade as the tip popped the red balloon.

97

Crimson splattered, blood and balloon spewed under the wax light like a scarlet scarf exploded out of my father's throat.

I pulled my sister's little body close to me, planting her pigtailed head against my stomach.

The audience gasped and screamed. Women's wails shrieked and echoed against the back of the stage. I didn't turn to look. I didn't avert my gaze from the plywood prison. My eyes flickered their focus from balloon to blood to my father's body. I had popped all of the balloons.

"And that is why children should not be allowed to play with knives," I heard a woman's voice croak inbetween the crowd's screams that were muffled behind their cupped hands.

My chapped lips carved a smirk across my mouth. I *never* missed my target.

GLOW WORMS

Creative Nonfiction

Lorraine Jeffery

"Fairies and treasure! Crimony! You're ten, Evelyn, do you really believe all that stuff?" Sam's warm brown eyes crinkled as he laughed.

I idolized my handsome fifteen-year old brother, but no one was quicker to put me in my place than Sam. I stopped on the dirt path in front of him and turned to face him. "You've never seen China," I stated with my hands on my hips. "But you say you know it's there. Just because we can't see them, doesn't mean they're not there."

Sam shook his head, grinned and walked around me. The path through the Oregon woods was narrow and I fell in step behind him. We were skirting a wild blackberry bush when I asked, "Do you think Dad will get a job at Pendleton's."

"Nope,"

"Why not?" I asked.

99

"We're in the middle of a Depression and every Tom, Dick and Harry is looking for a job—and there's Dad with his bum wrist. They'll just hire some guy who looks big and strong."

"Daddy's strong," I said hotly.

"Yeah, I know that," he said, stopping where the trail widened, and sitting down on a fallen log. "But *they* don't know that."

I nodded and sat beside him, unconsciously brushing dust off my too-big overalls. "If Daddy got a job, maybe Muma would be happier."

"Nope," Sam said.

"Gosh, can't you say anything good?"

"She's sick. That thing on her neck is a goiter and she needs an operation."

"But if we had money for doctors, they could make her better."

"Maybe," he said, unconsciously brushing loose bark off of the log next to him. "I think I can get a job with the CCCs and then I can help out."

"When?" I asked, frowning.

"As soon as I can."

"Don't you have to be eighteen?"

"Used to be," he said. "But they've lowered the age to seventeen. And sometimes boys lie when they look old enough." I looked at him, wondering if he would lie and wondering if he looked seventeen.

"Well, that wood's not going to chop itself," he said, standing up abruptly. "Are you coming?"

"In a while," I said. He nodded and kicked a pine cone

out of his way as he continued down the path.

"Would you have to live away from home?" I asked his retreating back.

"Maybe," he said, and then turned back and grinned at me. "Better keep looking for that treasure."

I nodded and walked slowly after him thinking about work and money and my mother. Muma scared me. When she yelled, screamed and threatened to kill herself, it was like an arctic wind blew in and froze everything inside of me. *Was that because of the goiter?*

A squirrel chattered in the top of a huge chinquapin tree and I stopped in the path and watched him. My mind went back to when I had first glimpsed the tall trees of Oregon. They were a change from the gray-blue sage, greasewoods, and mesquite of Utah. Aunt Evaline and Uncle Henry had come with us from Utah and Aunt Evaline and Muma had laughed as they prepared meals together while Daddy, Uncle Henry and Uncle Tom built the 16x20 foot one-room house. Muma had even helped nail the flattened cardboard boxes that would form the inside walls, onto the two-by-fours. And I remembered her excitement when they felled the logs to build our permanent house. But that had been three years earlier and Muma had been happier then.

I rounded a salal bush and crouched down to look at the small hole at the bottom of the fir tree where the large roots spread like tentacles on the ground.

"What ya lookin for?" asked a voice above me. I glanced up at spindly legs sticking out from too-short overalls. *She'll be next to get the overalls I've got on*, I thought.

My younger sister, Lela had caught me peering into the hole in the tree roots.

"Nothing," I muttered.

"Looking for fairies?" she asked with a trace of sarcasm.

"Well, I think there really are fairies," I said, cautiously standing up, "but they're good at hiding from us."

Lela looked skeptical. "But, how do you know if you haven't seen them?"

"I have seen them in books. And I thought I glimpsed them one time down by the creek—but I'm not sure."

Lela sighed and put her hand on her hip, as she had seen our mother do. "Muma said you have a big imagination."

I nodded. *Muma would say that.*

"What do fairies look like?" she asked, scuffing her bare feet in the dust.

"They're just like tiny people with beautiful wings. In the book at school, the mother fairy's dress was yellow and white, even prettier than the blue dress Mrs. Holmquist has, and they had a tiny house. There was a tiny davenport and tables and chairs, and their walls were gold colored. They even had a tiny fire in the fireplace."

"But that was a picture in a book," Lela said.

"Yeah, but one day when I was playing, I saw a hole under a tree and I scrunched down and looked in. I saw something pink for just a second, and then it was gone. When I stood up, something moved in the branches of the same tree and I saw something red."

"Birds, maybe."

"There's nothing pink that lives in a hole," I said hotly.

"And we don't have red birds around here."

Lela chewed her lip. "Even if they're real and you see them, no one will believe you."

I nodded. "Yeah, but if they are real, maybe I could find their treasure. They always have a treasure."

"What kind of treasure?" she asked.

I shrugged. "Jewels and stuff, I guess. But whatever it is, I would use it to buy a new house."

Lela picked up a stick and drew a circle in the dust. "I've never seen any fairies. All I've seen in the woods are bugs and squirrels, and lots of snails and slugs," she said, grimacing.

"And flowers. There are flowers," I reminded her.

She nodded getting into the game. "And cows and skunks. But they're Johnson's cows. I wish we had our own. Then Dad wouldn't have to buy milk from them."

"Leeela. Leeela," someone called from the house.

"Della probably wants you to watch Aaron for a while," I said.

Lela stuck out her lower lip. "Why do I always have to?"

"Hey, I took care of him all last week. It's your turn."

Lela frowned, but followed the path toward the house. I stood still listening to the rustle of the wind in the branches far above me. It sounded as if someone were whispering or singing softly. I loved my magical Oregon woods and I imagined the firs, pines and oaks protected the ferns, thimbleberry, Oregon grape and maple vine that grew under them. They also guarded the fairies, elves and other fantastic beings that lived there—just beyond my view.

As I headed toward the house, I stopped at the graying stack of logs—logs for our permanent house. *Okay, they aren't cream-colored anymore*, I thought, *but castles are gray.* I remembered the castles in the worn story books at school—silver and turreted, with lights shining from all the windows. I walked closer to the logs and took a deep breath, but couldn't detect the fresh wood scent that I loved.

I was almost to the door of the house when I heard the bang of pots and pans. I knew what that meant. Della was cooking and she was mad—again.

She was lighting the coal oil lamp as I walked in. It flared. She adjusted it to banish the gloom of the small-windowed house. She wore overalls, like I did, but hers were cleaner and she had tied some red cloth around her waist like a belt. It looked pretty.

"Stir the gravy," she said. "And I'll slice the bread."

I stirred the milk gravy in the black pan, while she sliced the coarse brown bread and then called the family to supper.

My brothers and sister came in, still talking about school, and Muma got up slowly from her bed in the corner. She was wearing the same dress she had worn all week and it looked too big for her. I smiled at her, but she didn't notice.

"Where's Daddy?" I asked as I sat down.

"He's at Sjogren's house," Muma said. "He'll be here when he's done."

Muma said the prayer and I started eating. I was hungry and the bread and gravy tasted good. I especially liked the taste of the salt on my tongue. I remembered the time Della had forgotten to salt the gravy and Sam had said it tasted like wallpaper paste. Della yelled at him telling him he should be happy to have anything to eat.

"I saw an owl today, up by the meadow," Sam said. "I think it may have a nest there."

Muma nodded. "I've been hearing them late at night."

I watched my mother poke at her food and listened to Sam talk about the owl and then the marbles he had won at school. Soon my sisters joined in—talking over each other. Aaron dropped some food on the floor.

Muma grabbed a rag from the stove and swiped at the food on the rough wood floor. "Can't you kids be quiet for even a minute?" she asked with an angry twist of her head. We quieted down.

I heard Daddy's soft footsteps just before he opened the door. He nodded to us and went to the bucket on the washstand to wash his hands. Daddy didn't talk much, so I wasn't surprised when he just sat down and started to eat.

Suddenly Lela straightened up in her chair and announced, "Daddy, Evelyn thinks there are fairies that live in the woods." I glared at her and kicked her under the table.

"Ouch!" Lela said, glaring at me and then looking at Daddy.

He finished chewing and looked over at me. "Fairies," he said. "To go along with elves and magic and treasure?" My face got hot and I looked down at my plate.

"Nothing wrong with fairies and elves," he said, as he took another bite of food. A warm wave of love flooded my body.

I had relaxed in my chair just as Della leaned forward. "When are we going to build the new house?" she asked. "I hate this old shack."

I quit chewing and fear clamped down on my stomach. I couldn't swallow. Muma quit eating too and looked hard at Della. "Well, if it's up to your father, we never will," she said loudly. "But if you're so smart, Missy, maybe you can tell me where we'd get the money."

Della dropped her eyes. "I don't know, but it's been three years."

"I don't know either. Maybe next spring," her mother replied. "I'm too tired and sick to talk about it."

"As usual," Della said under her breath.

Muma stood up suddenly and hit the table, rattling the mismatched plates. "You don't give a damn anyway," she shouted. "None of you care whether I live or die." She turned and stalked back to her bed. I was still looking at my plate, when I heard the bed springs creak. My mouth was full of saliva and I finally managed to swallow.

"Well, when Dad?" Della pressed.

"Don't rightly know," Daddy replied between regular bites. "When we get the money, I suppose."

"We'll never get the money!" Della screamed. "We'll never get out of here!" Her fork clattered on the table as she jerked up and ran outside, slamming the door behind her. I sat at the table and watched Lela's jerky motions as she finished eating.

I washed the dishes and hung the wet flour sack by the window to dry. Then I went outside and looked for Della. When I couldn't find her, I walked over to the big fir stump where Sam was sitting and carving an oak branch.

"What're you making?" I asked.

"A whistle," he replied, and blew some sawdust out of the hole he was gouging.

"Where's Della?"

"Off in the woods somewhere," he said. "She'll be back."

"She's always mad," I said softly.

"Well yeah," he said, putting down the whistle to pick a fir sliver out of his thumb. "But, she hates it here. Eddie says that she won't tell anybody at high school where she lives. Maybe she's hoping for a new house, but I don't think we're going to get one."

"We are," I said suddenly. "We are—someday. And it will be a silver house."

"A silver house?"

"Yeah," I said pointing to the stack of logs. "Those logs used to be yellow, but now they've turned silver. If Daddy uses those to build our house it will be silver, like a castle."

Sam glanced at the logs. "For crying out loud, they aren't silver. They're just gray, because they've been there so long."

"I think they're pretty. Muma would be happy in a silver house."

Sam sighed. "We can't build a house without a well," he said slowly. Dad dug three times and never did hit water and we can't live here without water."

"But we could get a real well-digging guy and he could find water. It's got to be here somewhere and besides, the water that Daddy brings home in the barrel isn't so bad."

He grimaced and shook his head. "It is bad and we can't haul water forever. And you know we don't have the money for a 'well-digging guy.'"

I nodded and we sat in silence and watched as darkness covered the maple vines and ferns nestling under the tall trees.

During the next two months, Muma slept most of the time and I quit going to her bed to tell her about what I had done that day. It was July when Della told me Muma was going to a hospital.

"It's a county hospital," she confided in hushed tones. "A place where poor people go who can't afford to pay." I didn't have to be told that this was "family business" and should stay that way.

Two weeks later, I watched as Daddy put his arm around Muma's skinny waist and help her into our noisy truck. I sat on the bed with my legs pulled up to my chin and listened until I could no longer hear the chug of the truck motor echoing off the tall trees. I wondered if the hospital would help. I wondered if Muma would stop threatening to kill herself and be like other mothers.

In late August, our entire family went to pick prunes in the large orchards, just outside of Elgarose, Oregon. The owners of the orchards shipped prunes all over the country and our family was grateful for the seasonal work. Some people came from far away and camped while they picked the prunes, but we were able to live at home. The work was hard and dirty, but we were excited about earning money for the family.

I was tired and sore at the end of each day, but I knew I wasn't as tired as my father because he was the one lifting and stacking the heavy boxes of prunes that others had filled. I also knew that he would wrap his wrist in a warm cloth and massage it when we got home each night. But the prune money would help us pay the bill we owed at Henry Swenson's grocery store and maybe buy new shoes for everyone.

It was soon after the prune harvest that my sisters and I started canning fruit for the winter. One of my jobs was to carry the apple peels and moldy blackberries out to the compost pile behind the house. The big pile of rotting fruit was blanketed with yellow jackets and when I threw the peels on the pile, I backed away quickly as the cloud of yellow jackets rose into the air. I held still and waited for the bees to settle down, before walking back to the house. My back ached, and I was anxious for school to start.

In September, we returned to the two-room school in Elgarose, and once again, the grazing milk cows raised their heads each morning at the school bell clanged. Della didn't come with us though. Without a mother at home, someone had to do the cooking and cleaning, so Della and Sam agreed to alternate years—one year at school and one year at home. The year I turned eleven, Della stayed home while Daddy looked for more work.

And it was just after school started when Daddy told us Muma was getting better and would be coming home in November. The knot in my stomach relaxed and was gone—the knot I hadn't known was there.

It was the last Friday of October when my best friend Barbara brought her lunch pail and sat down next to me on the bench in the covered play area at school.

"Are you moving?" she asked without preamble. "Belle told me your family was going to rent the house behind the school. If you did, you wouldn't have to walk so far."

I almost choked on my homemade brown bread and jam. *What was she talking about? I didn't want to move.*

"I don't know," I mumbled. "Della and Sam haven't said anything."

"If you moved now, you'd be there when your Mom got home from the hospital," Barbara continued.

My eyelid twitched. I hadn't told Barbara anything about "our family business," but as I looked at her, I saw no judgement—only curiosity.

"I'll find out," I said, putting my uneaten sandwich back in my lunch pail.

As I walked home that afternoon, I couldn't think of anything other than the possible move. I knew living by the schoolhouse would be very different than living in my woods. It was only four miles from where I currently lived, but it was in the middle of fields that belonged to someone else. There were little wooded areas, but they belonged to someone else too. There would be no fairies there.

When I got home, Della was hanging out wash behind the house. I waited while she hung two flour-sack towels and Daddy's brown pants on the line that was stretched between two fir trees.

Finally, I took a breath and began. "Barbara said we're going to move to the house behind the school."

Della turned and grimaced. "I don't know whether I'm supposed to tell you, but I think we are. The new house has six rooms and real walls. One of the rooms even has wallpaper in it."

Tears stung my eyelids and I looked at the ground. I didn't care about six rooms or wallpaper. "Are we going to sell this place?"

"To who?" Della snorted. "Nobody has any money and it's not a real house anyway. We'll probably just leave it." Those were such sad words to me. *How could we just walk off and leave our house and our woods?*

I played by myself that afternoon, down by the creek. I gathered acorns, carefully removed their caps, stuck them upside down in the moss near the creek and arranged them in a circle. I picked some berries from a nearby salal bush and dropped one in each acorn cup. Then I dipped my hand in the creek and let a few drops of water from my fingers fall into the same cups.

"Okay fairies, you can come and eat now," I said out loud, but I wasn't surprised no winged people appeared. I spent the next half hour building a little bark roof over the cups, and then Della called us in for supper.

We ate the two quarts of applesauce that hadn't sealed and a loaf of homemade bread that night. It was dark by the time we'd finished, but the house was small and the night air was cool, so we went back outside to play kick the can.

I was thinking of other things and I got tired of always being the first one caught, so I walked off by myself into the trees until the shouts of my brothers and sisters were like the low buzz of a classroom. I could see shafts of moonlight between the trees and glanced back toward the house. Yes, I could still see the faint light from the small window next to the door.

I wandered into an area where the Oregon grape, thimbleberries and scrub oak had been cleared away. Even the ferns were gone, and the lacy shadows of the pines arched above me like the high ceiling of a beautiful ballroom. I closed my eyes, held out my imaginary skirt and curtsied to my partner. And then I was dancing. Droopy pine needles interspersed with stars formed the jeweled canopy above me. I closed my eyes and the woods were full of elves, butterflies, fairies and wondrous treasure. I could see the pinks of the lady slippers that grew on the mossy bank of the creek, the yellows of buttercups and the purples of wild violets. As I whirled, I arched my arms over my head, as I had seen in the books at school. And I could hear music, quick notes from a violin—elfin music.

Suddenly I was falling, and I hit the ground hard. I had tripped over a protruding root, but I was still smiling as I stood up. It was then that I saw the tiny moving lights on the old log. *Maybe I bumped my head really hard,*

I thought. I closed my eyes and then slowly opened them. The tiny lights were still there—bobbing and dipping on the log.

They seemed to be swaying in mid-air, like lanterns on the English carriages I had seen in books at school. My breath came quickly as I cupped both hands together and gently gathered as many of the sparkling jewels as I could. Then I ran for the house. I was out of breath as I pushed open the door, talking as I came into the room.

"Della, see what I found," I said, opening my hands. And then I screamed, as a dozen brown, jointed bugs dropped onto the wooden table.

"But they made light," I said. "They sparkled. They really did. They were like treasure and I gathered them and . . "

"What's wrong?" Sam came bursting through the door with Lela and Aaron close behind him.

"Evelyn found some kind of bug that makes a light or something," Della said, looking with disgust at the caterpillar-shaped creatures as they crawled across the table and fell on the floor.

"Oh, they're called glow worms," Sam said, as his eyes lit up. "They're hard to find. I've only seen them once before." Then he paused and looked at me, "What did you think they were?"

Tears were welling up in my eyes and I was trying to stop them from sliding down my cheeks. "I don't know. They were just pretty and I, I thought. . " but I couldn't finish.

I brushed past Sam and ran back into the woods. I scooted under the low branches of a fir tree, careful not to get pitch from the trunk on my clothes. And then I cried into the dry needles on the ground. *How could ugly brown bugs make such pretty, moving lights–almost like stars caught in a spider's web? But they weren't stars or fairies or anything else magical—they were just brown bugs.*

I was still under the tree when I heard the crunch of my father's steady footsteps in the leaves. I crawled out from under the tree and wiped my face with the backs of my hands. Daddy came through the trees carrying a pail of warm milk in each hand and I hurried over to carry one of them.

"Much obliged," he said, ruffling my hair with his free hand.

As we walked past the stack of gray logs, I could see the light from the open door of the house. Della was kneeling and pushing bottles of applesauce and blackberry jam under the beds.

We moved to the new house the first week of November. We didn't have much, so we moved everything in one day. I helped Sam carry the iron bedstead into the house behind the school. The wallpaper was peeling in a few places and the kitchen needed paint, but it had three bedrooms and plastered walls. I wondered if the new house would make our family different. I wondered if Muma would be happier here.

I volunteered to go back for the last load with Daddy. We didn't talk over the steady grind of the truck motor. While he loaded the last crates into the truck, I walked back into my woods.

I looked at the browning leaves on some of the oak trees, and the rotting logs in the undergrowth. I thought about the poison oak and skunk cabbage sprinkled among the ferns, deeper in the woods.

I stood listening. I could hear the wind through the needles of the fir and pine trees, but only the wind—no fairy music. And as I walked back to the truck, I heard only the dry grating sound of the dead leaves. Once a twig snapped behind me, but I didn't turn around. I rode back on the flatbed of the truck, my legs dangling over the end, watching until my trees melted into cultivated fields.

A CHARMED LIFE

CREATIVE NONFICTION

D. A. Gordon

QUIET AIR, QUIET GRASS, QUIET street. I glance at the pregnant moon. Tonight even the heavens are quiet, as though the universe is holding its breath. For me? That's possible. Perhaps my stricken soul has frustrated the normal flow.

I take a sip of tea and notice my ice cubes have melted. Maybe they were afraid of clinking against the glass and disturbing the peace. I move and the new-mown grass tickles my bare legs. The more things change, the more they stay the same. Here I am, spending the evening sitting in the yard, one speck of humanity, one of six billion, waiting for the other shoe to drop.

That proverbial other shoe—the other half of something already unlucky, unwanted, or sad. I shift my butt, sip my weak tea and wonder about that second shoe. I feel it teetering on the brink, getting ready to drop. I nod.

Bring it on, I think. Let's get this over with. While pondering which unhappy volley would hit me next, I sense movement down the street. I stop breathing and stare. What if it's a snake? Should I head for the house? I can't see much on that dark macadam and yet I know something moved. I narrow my stare. There, it moved again.

In the center of this flattened strip of tar and rock something is moving. When I see it move again I almost laugh aloud because whatever it is, it's hopping. Good grief, Charlie Brown, it's a toad, and it's not just any toad but the biggest one I've ever seen. A big toad right here in my neighborhood, hopping up the middle of the road in the dark of night. I wonder why it's doing that. If I weren't sitting at ground level I might not have caught the movement until the toad jumped right next to me. Well, better a toad than a snake. I relax.

The homely critter hops three or four times and then sits on its lumpy haunches for five or ten seconds before it hops again. Always after the hops come the rest. What an odd way to travel, I think. It seems terribly inefficient, but since I've never been a toad, what do I know?

As I watch the bumpy amphibian hop up the slight grade, I replace thinking of that other shoe hovering over me with worry over the toad's safety. I yearn to get the creature out of danger, but I don't know how to do it. If only I could explain that although this roadway appears quiet, the middle of the road is a dangerous place to be, especially for something so small. I want him to move to the sidewalk. Because I spotted the toad and I'm watching it, I feel somewhat responsible for its well-being, yet there is was no way a middle-aged, squeamish female like me is going to go over there and pick it up.

Absolutely no way.

So there we are, the three of us: moon, toad and me. As the serene evening wears on, the moon continues to rise, the toad continues to hop and rest, and I continue to watch them both. Of the three of us, I am the only one growing nervous.

I am so intent on the toad's slow journey that I nearly drop my tea when the sound of a motor breaks the silence. Just as I feared, a vehicle with dim headlights turns the corner and starts up the hill toward the oblivious toad. As the small pickup draws closer to the dark lump, I consider waving my arms or running into the street to force the driver to veer around the creature, but then I wonder how smart that would be. No telling what the driver might do if a half-crazed woman jumped up from the grass and ran toward him at ten o'clock at night. He might panic. I could just see the headlines: *Woman Panics Driver, Causes Accident*. So I remain where I am.

Alas, the hapless critter is on its own.

As the truck nears the toad, I do what most cowards do: I cover my eyes. I hate myself for it, but there it is. After I hear the truck pass, I inch my hands from my face. Although I fear the worst, that I will see a squashed body on the asphalt and feel like wretching retching, I must look.

The truck is gone and I'm scanning the pavement when I see movement again. There it is, that lumpy amphibian is still making its slow progress up the road with a hop,

hop, hop, hop—rest. I gasp. The toad made it! My arms shoot into the air and I almost yell.

Although Vitt Drive doesn't get much traffic, especially on a Thursday night, all of the residents own an automobile. As the toad continues its slow progression up the hill, my shoulders tense every time I hear a vehicle. At any moment another driver might turn onto Vitt. I check the moon and finish my tea, but I am not about to leave. Like an adventure junkie, I need to stay with this story to the end.

Just before the lumpy critter passes my way, it alters its course. Now it's heading toward the opposite side of the road. Hop, hop, hop, hop—rest. If the hesitant traveler could just make it to the curb, it would be out of danger—from cars, anyway. Like an avid fan, I'm rooting for the little guy.

"Hurry toad," I whisper. "Move it. Don't you have a faster gear?" But the toad pays me no heed. It continues the same laborious hopping and resting sequence it has followed all evening. I groan.

Before the toad makes much progress toward the curb, a blue sedan turns the corner and drives our way. I glance from the toad to the car, back and forth. Could the toad survive another encounter with four looming tires? Would it reach the curb in time?

Probably not. It's too slow to compete on a road used by automobiles. The toad has lived long enough to grow to a good size, has taken chances and faced danger before, but apparently his number would be up tonight.

Once again I cringe and cover my eyes, wishing I could cover my ears as well. I don't want to know what a tire squashing a toad sounds like. After the car passes, I lower my hands to look for a dark wet spot on the pavement. Yet once again the lethal tires missed the brazen little creature. I relax my shoulders and sigh. How could that toad be so lucky? I don't know, but I'm immensely pleased when it hops off the blacktop, over the curb, and onto the neighbor's grass.

Oddly enough, now that it is out of mortal danger, it moves faster. You fool, I think. Why do you hop faster now? As though someone is prodding it, that toad hops over the short grass without resting. It just keeps hopping across the lawn, over a border of smooth rocks, and into my neighbor's garden. Just like that, the determined little guy disappears from sight. Maybe the garden had been its goal all along and it sped up during the final stretch. Maybe it has a friend in that garden, or a partner. Maybe that's where it lives.

I stare at the garden and wonder about the creature's trip up that dangerous road in the dark. The toad's journey to the garden seemed ordained, and this evening at least, the little guy's life has been charmed.

A blessed toad... who would have thought?

If a creature like a toad can be charmed, perhaps that other shoe isn't ready to fall after all.

ABOUT THE AUTHORS

JAMES D. BEERS IS A self-employed archaeologist, part-time humor, ghost story, and young adult fiction writer, and frequent stress eater living in Northern Utah with his wife, Jenna, and son, Joseph. He loves ice cream, steak, and driving questionable two-track roads in the wilderness. His writerly side is chronicled on his website, writingwithbeers.com, and his first collection of humorous short stories is A Knack for Embarrassment, published in 2016.

ROBYN BUTTERFIELD, AN AWARD-WINNING AUTHOR, composer, and poet, lives with her husband in northern Utah. They are the parents of six children.

NEIL DABB HAS BEEN A freelance writer since his early college days and has been published in a wide variety of magazines. He has self published over a dozen novellas and two anthologies as well as several of his father's works. He is an amateur blacksmith, father of 5 children and 5 1/2 grandchildren, and an amateur radio operator.

DENIS FEEHAN IS A MEMBER of the Utah Poet's Society in St. George as well as a fiction writer with the Heritage Writers Group in that city. In his spare time, he plays keyboards in a local band (in Mesquite, NV) and is an Actor/Director with at the Mesquite Community Theater.

CASEY GASPER LIVES WITH HER husband and kids in beautiful Utah. She enjoys writing because it can be done in her jammies, and she excels at keeping her kids alive.

D.A. GORDON LIVES IN SOUTHERN Utah where she writes, copy edits, and publishes both fiction and non-fiction. She mostly pens short stories, articles, and creative nonfiction. Currently she is working on a nonfiction how-to book and a collection of short stories.

JOSIE HULME IS A LIFE-LONG voracious reader and enthusiastic writer. To her, being a writer is one of the best jobs in the world—second only to being a wife and the mother of five children. She lives in North Ogden and spends half her day writing in blissful quiet when the kids are at school and the other half being overwhelmed with "Hey, mom!"s, driving, homework, activities, music practice, dinner prep, noise, and love when the kids come home.

C.H. HUNG GREW UP AMONG the musty book stacks of public libraries, where she found a lifelong love for good stories and lost 20/20 vision for good. After a brief stint dabbling in reality, C.H. Hung re-entered the world of myth and fantasy to finally put to paper the dreams and stories she's carried in her head since those long-ago days in the library.

LORRAINE JEFFERY HAS WON POETRY prizes in state and national contests and has published over fifty poems in various publications, including *Clockhouse, Ibbetson Street, Rockhurst Review, Calliope* and *Kindred*. She has also published short stories, articles and a mystery novel. She is the mother of ten children and lives with her husband in Orem.

BRITNEY JOHNSON IS THE CTO of RedBird metrics, a program that makes it easy to market products and services through social media. She graduated with a bachelors degree in Management Information Systems from Utah State.

THE ONLY THING TIM KELLER likes better than reading a good story is telling one. He always wanted to try his hand at writing and began work on the Great American Novel a couple of years ago. The ensuing obsession changed his life. Since then, he's branched out into short prose and essays. He even works on the novel from time to time.

SUE STEVENSON LETH HAS RETIRED from two separate careers, one in higher education and one in private business. She and her husband, Peter, moved to St. George to retire in 2012, loving every moment of blistering summers, monsoon rains, brilliant blue skies, and especially enjoying the exquisite endangered specie of Bearclaw Poppy that grows on surrounding hillsides near their residence. Sue is currently a member of Utah State Poetry Society, Redrock Writers, Dixie Poets and Heritage Writers Guild, and the League of Utah Writers. Her poetry appears in *Utah Sings, an Anthology of Contemporary Poetry*, and the Arizona State Poetry Society's *Sandcutters Chapbook*.

SHIRLEY MANNING HAS ENJOYED READING good writing since early in her life. She appreciates the language of carefully-chosen words, connecting and surprising us in delightful and profound ways.

ANNA MARASCO IS A LICENSED clinical social worker and utilizes her education and experience to realistically and empathetically portray human behavior and emotion in fiction and poetry. Anna's spare time is spent with the love of her life: her horse, Henry.

CHRIS TODD MILLER HAS UNWAVERING faith in the power of story well-told. The hope that if the favorite character of your favorite story dies, there's a chance that on the re-read she might just make it, and that your to-be-read stack can never be too tall. He loves BBQ, sea food, and top shelf whiskey. You have an open invitation to join him for a drink. He is the author of the award-winning novel, By Blood Bequeathed.

KERI MONTGOMERY WRITES MAINLY SPECULATIVE fiction with the occasional jaunt into suspense. When not writing, she enjoys fighting fire while wearing a yellow rookie helmet and strives to learn superhuman skills for real life domination. She runs a local chapter for the League of Utah Writers and uses "I'm researching for a novel" as an excuse to do exciting stuff firsthand. Her first published work is included in the non-fiction Amazon best-seller by Jodi Orgill Brown, *Rise Above Depression*. Someday, Keri plans to eat a Carolina Reaper pepper. That is, whenever she hits maximum on the bravery scale.

WHILE THIS IS **SARA MORTENSEN**'s first published work, she's been writing stories all her life. Presently, you can find her sifting through web data in her career as a digital marketer, though her unquiet mind and love of the written word keeps her tethered to her one true passion: writing nonfiction.

E.B. WHEELER IS THE AUTHOR of award-winning nonfiction and historical fiction, including *The Haunting of Springett Hall*. She is an adjunct history professor and consults about historic preservation. She lives in northern Utah with her husband, children, and various pets, and she tries to avoid places that might be haunted after dark.

JOHNNY WORTHEN GREW UP IN the high desert snows and warm summer winds of the Wasatch Mountains. He graduated with a B.A. in English, minor in Classics and a Master's in American Studies from the University of Utah.

After a series of businesses and adventures, including years abroad and running his own bakery, Johnny found himself drawn to the only thing he ever wanted to do -- write. And write he does. Well versed in modern literary criticism and cultural studies, Johnny writes upmarket multi-genre fiction – thriller, horror, young adult, comedy and mystery so far.

Made in the USA
San Bernardino, CA
15 August 2018